I CAN'T PLACE THIS PLACE AT ALL:

Working with people with dementia and their carers

Mary Marshall

VENTURE PRESS

Published by
VENTURE PRESS
16 Kent Street
Birmingham
B5 6RD
Tel: 0121 622 3911

British Library Cataloguing-in-Publication Data.
A catalogue record for this book is available from the British Library

The photograph on the front cover appears by kind permission of Alzheimer Scotland - Action on Dementia.

ISBN 1 873878 13 3 (paperback)

Printed in Great Britain

Cover Design by Western Arts
194 Goswell Road
London EC1V 7DT

This book is dedicated to the one in ten of us who will get dementia and to those who will care for us.

Acknowledgements

This book could not have been written without the willingness of a great many people to share their knowledge and their experience with me. My colleagues at the Dementia Services Development Centre are a constant source of inspiration. Many other relatives, colleagues and friends in the UK and Australia have contributed, not least with anecdotes which, heavily disguised, form the individual stories in this book. My thanks to all of them, especially Carole Archibald, Mary Dixon and Sylvia Woolfe; I hope they feel pleased that their expertise is there to help others understand how we can work better with people with dementia and their carers. Thanks too to Alan Dunlop for the diagram and John Killick for the poem.

FIND ME!

I can't place
this place at all . . .
isn't that terrible?

What street is this
what town, where is
the nearest post office?

Can you take me
home so far?
I'll reward you

I can't find
that label with my
name and address

Find me! Find me!
I wish to God
God would do something!

John Killick crafted this poem from a transcript of a conversation with a resident with dementia. He is Writer in Residence for Westminster Health Care.

Contents

Introduction

This book is for anyone working with people with dementia. It is written for those who are starting in the field, but may also offer something to more experienced staff. It is written for any kind of non-medical staff. It may have something to offer medics, but it will not cover the use of medication. It is written for staff in any setting: shortstay, longstay, daycare, domiciliary care and for staff at any level - managers or frontline.

The reason for suggesting such a broad range of staff is that there are basic approaches and principles of care that apply to any care of people with dementia. They are the need to see people with dementia as whole people with bodies as well as brains, with histories as well as a present, with the same needs as the rest of us for physical contact, spiritual experience and self-esteem as well as food, warmth and safety. It is the application of these principles to practice which is such a struggle. We work in complex worlds and dementia is a complex illness.

Our worlds are complex because we provide care in constantly changing organisations. The organisations are full of conflicting priorities, sometimes between different needy groups and sometimes between quality and cost. People with dementia can easily slip to the bottom of the priority pile because they have no political clout at all. They usually combine being old, being unable to speak for themselves, being female in the main, and having a progressive illness. All reasons why an investment in their care is often felt to be a waste of money, compared with other groups such as adults of working age or children. Phair and Good (1995) have an excellent chapter on attitudes in this field of work.

It is a complex illness because it cannot be understood or managed in isolation. Just about everything affects it. There has even been research into whether the phases of the moon affect the behaviour of people with dementia!

Following on from this is the need to be careful about the language we use. If we refer to "the demented" or "demented people" there is a danger that we are seeing their dementia as their main characteristic, whereas they are people with an illness. Using the term "people with dementia" reminds us that they are people. Behind the use of terms such as "the demented" can be attempts to distance oneself from these sick and often plainly unhappy people. The words "suffering from dementia" are kinder but fail to recognise that many of the people around the person with dementia suffer too, especially the main carer. Speaking of which, this book will use the word "carer" for anyone providing care as a relative or friend, and worker or staff for those who are paid or volunteers. This may not please some readers who rightly hold that the issues are often the same whether you are paid or not and that people who are paid do care; nevertheless it seems worth making a distinction.

Finally, a word about the way this book is organised. It is in sections: there seems no other way. An inevitable distortion creeps in because the sections seem to carve up a world which is in reality so interrelated. The sections also often overlap since the same issues are dealt with under different headings.

I lean towards an ecological or systems approach to everything. If you alter one system, the whole lot alters because everything affects everything else. Dividing the book into sections also conceals the common threads that underlie everything. I have already mentioned principles of care. Communication is another unifying thread. Communicating with people with dementia, with carers, with colleagues, with the public: all are central to improving care of people with dementia. However, in spite of a predisposition for an ecological model, this book will still have to be split into sections.

It may also tend to use Scottish terminology because many of the individuals, whose stories illustrate the text, live in Scotland. Thus terms such as "social work department" or "health board" may be used instead of the terms for England, Wales or Northern Ireland. For older people these statutory agencies are broadly similar in their responsibilities although there are some differences in the levels and types of provision.

Chapter 1
The New Culture of Dementia Care

What is the new culture?

A brief chapter at the beginning of this book describing the values and the approach to be adopted is appropriate since, in the middle 1990s, we seem to be in the midst of rethinking the whole pattern of care. Our view of the disease itself and what is required from services and staff is changing fundamentally. Tom Kitwood and Sue Benson (1995) have written and collected papers from a group of experts in a book that uses the term "a new culture". This notion of a new culture is helpful since we are seeing change at every level: the understanding of the disease, the nature of the skills required, the design and style of services, and so on. There are a lot of contributory factors in this gradual but incontrovertible change of culture. We have a great deal more experience than we had ten or fifteen years ago when there were fewer people with dementia. We are constantly learning from the experience of increasing numbers of staff and carers, as well as from people with dementia themselves.

There have been some energetic exponents of new approaches. Tom Kitwood himself is a prolific writer for a number of audiences. The eloquent book he and Kathleen Bredin wrote (1992) has been hugely influential in emphasising the need to see the personhood of people with dementia and it is mentioned more fully in the next chapter. This book has put into words the feelings of a lot of people in the field that we are dealing with people who, given good care, can be assisted in retaining their skills, personalities and quality of life to a remarkable degree. Indeed in some circumstances they can regain these, hence the concept of rementia. Although we are all taught that dementia is a progressive and inexorable decline into helplessness, many of us have learned that reality is far more complex and that far more potential remains than we can be led to believe. The new culture is in good part about learning what we have yet to learn; how little we know about the impact of neurological damage on people's functioning.

The shift away from the traditional view of dementia being a diagnosis of hopelessness and helplessness is slow and having little impact in many settings, but a momentum is gathering. It is increasingly unlikely that policy makers, planners, managers and staff in any setting will be unaware of the wind of change. Whether they choose to take any notice is quite another matter.

The aim of this book is to introduce some of the implications of a more positive approach in a readable and jargon-free fashion. I find it very helpful, as you can see from the dedication, to think in terms of the possibility that I shall get dementia.

The extent to which the culture of care changes in terms of buildings and staff approaches will affect the care I receive. It is very easy to think of dementia as "their" problem rather than my problem. Tom Kitwood adds to this way of thinking the notion that a major force in the incapacity of many people with dementia is the way we relate to them: that it is our problem not their problem. Starting with ourselves means that we need to strive for a degree of empathy. We will be helped if we imagine ourselves with the disease and consider what would be the most help to us.

Some readers will immediately think that what would be the most help would be a dose of poison but I think this view is to misunderstand the way that we, as individuals, cope with increasing disability. It is usually only when pain is intolerable that we consider ending our lives. The belief that we shall want to end our lives if we get dementia is, I think, based on the experience we all have of seeing people with dementia receive the most degrading care which emphasises incompetence and hopelessness. Seeing good care that respects individuality and builds on remaining competence, can be very encouraging. This is not to underestimate the awfulness of having a diseased brain, but an attempt to see it as any other sort of terminal illness: awful but part of life.

The new culture of dementia care is a very exciting one for those of us who are involved. Every day new approaches are being tried, many transferred from other fields. There are constant advances in our expertise. This book can only cover the understandings and knowledge I have accumulated to date. It is written in full awareness of my limited knowledge and of the speed of change. My intention is that it communicates a spirit of optimism and excitement that encourages readers to be constantly alert to new approaches and to share the process of learning.

Dementia as a disability
I have found it very helpful to see dementia as a disability. It somehow brings it into the realms of calm consideration rather than fear and helplessness. Dementia as a disability is characterised by:

- failing memory
- impaired learning
- impaired ability to reason
- high levels of stress
- acute sensitivity to the social and built environment.

In my view the acute sensitivity to the social and the built environment is akin to the acute sensitivity blind people have to hearing. It seems to me that if you cannot remember and cannot work out what is going on you are acutely dependent on buildings and the people around you to "tell" you in some way.

If we accept that dementia is a disability then we have to adopt a rehabilitative approach. We can turn to a vast literature about rehabilitation from the world of disability. Mair (1972) provides the most often quoted definition of rehabilitation: "restoration of patients to their fullest physical, mental and social capability." Mattingly (1981) adds a set of other qualities of rehabilitation which are very relevant here: "prevention of avoidable disability; the restoration of physical and mental health; the provision of aids and appliances; and resettlement into the community."

Prevention of avoidable disability is a very useful concept in dementia care since so much of what we do is actually disabling rather than therapeutic. Somehow we need to be able to explain to purchasers and providers of care that if we do not provide the right kind of care people will be more disabled and dependent than they need to be. This is a strong argument for the best buildings and the most skilled staff given what we know about the sensitivity of people with dementia to the social and the built environment.

The restoration of physical and mental health is important and will be mentioned again in this book. Many people with dementia experience untreated physical and mental illness which is wrongly attributed to the dementia. Such illnesses can fundamentally affect the capacity of people with dementia to function at their optimum level.

The provision of aids and appliances will be covered in this book under the headings of design and technology. Resettlement into the community is seldom a rehabilitation aim for people with dementia unless we emphasise their need to live somewhere as familiar as possible if they are to cope as well as they can.

The standard text on rehabilitation of older people is Andrews (1991). He points out that there are special factors in this field which need consideration: multiple pathology, polypharmacy, mental vulnerability, personality traits, low expectations, social vulnerability, carers and the team concept. These are very useful factors to bear in mind and they will be mentioned later in this book. The team concept is always a key feature of rehabilitation and this is very true for dementia care. Disappointingly he does not focus on dementia itself being a focus for rehabilitation. Perhaps he is not yet aware of the new culture of dementia care.

Readers may think it is somewhat far-fetched to think of rehabilitation in relation to a progressive disease and I would be the first to admit that there has to be a balance between palliative care and rehabilitation. However, it is interesting to find that people who work in the field of terminal care talk about rehabilitation within palliative care. They talk about adding life to the time before death: a useful approach for us too.

This reminds me to mention another underpinning principle of this book which is that you cannot separate health and social care as far as dementia is concerned. Like much practice in the field of mental health the roles of health and of social care are inextricably intertwined. Helping people function at their highest possible level is everybody's task and is best done where all the expertise available is put to use.

Seeing dementia as a disability also makes it possible to relate to important literature about disability which identifies the attitudes of those surrounding the disabled person as a source of much disability (Oliver 1990). This is very helpful in looking at dementia. It also links it to important design principles such as "barrier free" (Martin 1992) or "Lifetime Homes". The key point I am trying to make is that it is helpful to see dementia as a disability if we are to learn the hard-won lessons from the world of disability. It also makes much of the new culture of care more understandable to a wider audience since concepts such as rehabilitation are well understood.

Transferring learning
A recurring theme of this book is that we are all learning all the time. This is why it is so exciting. One of the main sources of expertise comes from our colleagues in other fields of work. In the previous section I mentioned what we can learn from the world of disability which is most developed by and with work with young physically disabled people. There seems to me to be a need for a great deal more bridge building.

Sometimes there is a need for mutual learning with shared groups such as those with Down's syndrome and dementia or those with AIDS or HIV and dementia. We can learn a great deal from the world of learning disability. They are much further ahead of us in thinking through concepts of normalisation. They have a well-established tradition of units for people with high levels of challenging behaviour and there is much recent work on stress-reduction techniques. They are also well ahead in understanding the need for small units of accommodation. Issues of conflict of interest and priorities between people with learning disabilities and their relatives are an issue in that field from which we have much to learn. We should probably be keeping a close eye on changing attitudes to day care in this field too.

We have learnt much over the years from child care. Life-story work, for example, has a long track record for children who have only a shaky sense of identity. Boarding out is a service model being adapted for our field. The tension between dependence and independence is a familiar one for child care which is also fundamental in our field. Hospice care and oncology generally is a field from which we have much to learn. Workers within it have grappled with issues of sharing a diagnosis and the omnipresence of dying which have much to teach us. I feel strongly that we can learn much about conflict resolution from the experts in industrial relations and international relations which I go into in more detail in Chapter 2.

I mention these only as examples. It seems to me that we need to learn from anywhere we can. The lessons will need to be adapted and tested in our field but we can benefit from seeking out common concerns.

Fundamentally what we need is care which recognises the uniqueness of each individual and their carer(s) but at the same time benefits from as wide a trawl of knowledge and practice as possible. It is very difficult, very demanding and very rewarding for all concerned when it works.

Risk
No book on dementia care should omit a section on risk but I have to admit that this section was put into the book last of all because it seems to me that the very word "risk" raises anxiety levels to the point where many staff can no longer see the person. I hope that this book is all about risk management, but that it starts from what is best for the person and then considers what is achievable.

Much of the new culture of dementia care is about making the point that it is the way that we treat people with dementia that makes their behaviour so worrying and frightening. Much of this book is about communication and providing care which meets needs in a way that minimises the problems caused by such behaviour.

However, we cannot ignore the fact that sometimes we may have to provide control as well as care. This needs to be done openly, to be recorded carefully, and where necessary proper use made of the law. As staff we have a duty of care as well as a duty to respect people with dementia as fellow citizens. There is always a balance to be struck. I hope I have struck it in a way that is useful to readers by avoiding the word "risk" but not ignoring the dilemmas and skilled judgements that staff have to make.

Chapter 2
The Context in Which We Work

Demographic

There is a curious tradition in books about older people to start with demography. In a sense, numbers should not matter. This is a book about ideas, skills and expertise so the potential number of recipients is not a central theme. However, the point needs to be made clearly and forcefully that dementia is perhaps the key health issue for the end of the century in more developed countries. It is a relatively new issue. We are going to have to work hard and fast to ensure that we effectively communicate and share ideas, skills and expertise. The urgency of this will hit less developed countries in the next century. In the final chapter I look at what we might want to say to them on the basis of our experience.

The context in which we work includes the demographic trends. Dementia is much more common as we get older. Although one in ten of us who live to retirement age will get it, we are more likely to get it if we live into our eighties and nineties. At this age, as many as one in five of us have it. Given a surviving baby bulge before the First World War, we now have large numbers of people who are very old. At the same time, expectation of life for those over retirement age has increased, although this is of much less importance than the baby bulge in explaining what is happening.

Thus we have substantial numbers of older people with dementia and increasing numbers anticipated in the future. Combined with this, there are emerging younger groups, such as people with Down's syndrome, who are now living longer and most of whom get dementia in their forties or fifties. There are also small numbers of people with AIDS and HIV who get dementia. There have always been small numbers of younger people with dementia, usually Alzheimer's disease, and tiny numbers with rare conditions such as Creutzfeldt-Jakob disease and Pick's disease. Sadly, people with Korsakoff's syndrome, which is the result of alcohol abuse, have also always been with us.

Alongside the increase in very old people, we have a decrease in the next generation because the inter-war period was one of a very low birthrate. The birthrate did not really begin to climb until the 1950s. (This latest baby bulge is the explanation for the figures given for the projected increase in dementia in the 2030s. Many of the buildings we are now erecting and staff now being trained will still be in action.) At present we have an increase in the numbers of people with dementia in the very old age groups and we have a decrease in the numbers of carers. This explains why there are some carers who care for a succession of elderly relatives. Mrs James is a schoolteacher in her early sixties. Over the last ten years she has cared, until they died, for her husband's disabled aunt, her mother-in-law, her own mother and she is now looking after another of her husband's aunts who has dementia. She and her husband are the only adults in their generation in these two families. ·

What is dementia?
I have deliberately not started this chapter on context with the usual explanation about the illness itself. This is because details of the illness are often seen as more important than other factors whereas they are only one aspect; but knowledge of the illness or, more accurately, illnesses is essential for any staff.

Dementia is a term used to describe a set of diseases which have a similar effect on the brain, and consequences for the functioning of the individual. Except for Korsakoff's syndrome, they are all progressive, although they progress in different ways. Although everyone's pathway through the disease is different, there are overriding similarities. Murphy (1986) provides a useful definition: "Dementia is a group of progressive diseases of the brain that slowly affect all functions of the mind and lead to a deterioration in a person's ability to concentrate, remember and reason. It can affect every area of human thinking, feeling and behaviour" (p12).

There are two main types of dementia, and some people have both. The largest group are those with Alzheimer's disease: perhaps half of the population with dementia. Alzheimer's disease is, generally speaking, characterised by a steady global deterioration. The next largest group are those with multi-infarct dementia, which is caused by strokes in the brain. Their dementia proceeds in a less global way with steady periods and sudden deterioration as sections of the brain are affected. Other minor types include Creutzfeldt-Jakob disease and Lewy Body type dementia. Korsakoff's disease is the dementia caused by alcohol abuse. If it is treated it does not progress further, but people with this disease can be very mentally impaired, see Table 1.

The speed of deterioration for people with dementia is very variable, although it may be quicker in the younger age groups. Some people can have the disease for as long as ten years. Many people die of something else before the disease has worked its full course.

Table 1 CAUSES OF DEMENTIA

COMMON CAUSES OF DEMENTIA

- **Alzheimer's disease**

  Onset usually over the age of 45 years.
  Gradual onset, progressive, unremitting course.
  Slightly commoner in women than in men.
  Definitive diagnosis only made at post mortem.
  Global deterioration.

- **Multi-infarct dementia**

  Onset usually over the age of 45 years.
  Often sudden onset, with focal neurological signs.
  Slightly commoner in men than in women.
  Usually past history of cardiovascular pathology.
  Stepwise deterioration.
  Uneven decline in skills and personality change.

- **Lewy body dementia**

  Hallucinations and delusions prominent.
  May react adversely to phenothiazines.

RARE CAUSES OF DEMENTIA

TREATABLE

B12 deficiency

Behavioural and memory changes most prominent.
Long tract signs may be present.
May have peripheral neuropathy.
May have a megaloblastic anaemia.

Normal pressure hydrocephalus

Characteristic triad of dementia, ataxia and urinary incontinence

Hypothyroidism

Always consider.

Tumour

Primary or secondary.

UNTREATABLE

Frontal lobe type

Frontal lobe symptoms more prominent than memory loss.

Downs's syndrome

Alzheimer type changes are common in people with Down's syndrome as they approach middle age.

Creutzfeldt-Jacob disease

Rapidly progressive with long tract signs prominent.

AIDS

Dementia occurs as a late manifestation in some patients with AIDS.

Table 1 is reproduced from a guide for GPs published by the Alzheimer's Disease Society/The Dementia Services Development Centre (1995)

Table 2   CLINICAL FEATURES OF DEMENTIA, DEPRESSION AND ACUTE, CONFUSIONAL STATE

	DEMENTIA	ACUTE CONFUSIONAL STATE	DEPRESSION
Onset	insidious	acute	gradual
Duration	months/years	hours/days/??weeks	weeks/months
Course	stable and progressive MID usually stepwise	fluctuates: worse at night lucid periods	usually worse in mornings improves as day goes on.
Alertness	usually normal	fluctuates	normal
Orientation	may be normal: usually impaired for time/place	always impaired: time/place/person	usually normal
Memory	impaired recent and sometimes remote memory	recent impaired	recent may be impaired remote intact
Thoughts	slowed reduced interests perseverate	often paranoid and grandiose ? bizarre ideas and topics	usually slowed preoccupied by sad and hopeless thoughts
Perception	? normal hallucinations in 30-40% (often visual)	visual and auditory hallucinations common	mood congruent auditory hallucinations in 20%
Emotions	shallow, apathetic, labile ? irritable, careless	irritable, aggressive, fearful.	may be flat, unresponsive or sad and fearful may be irritable
Sleep	often disturbed. nocturnal wandering common nocturnal confusion	nocturnal confusion	early morning wakening
Other Features		other physical disease may not be obvious	? past history of mood disorder

Table 2 is reproduced from a guide for GPs published by the Alzheimer's Disease Society/The Dementia Services Development Centre (1995)

A diagnosis is essential, partly to determine the kind of dementia but also to make sure that the person actually has dementia. Many people experience loss of memory and disorientation when they are acutely ill or very distressed. This is known as delirium or an acute confusional state. Some medication can cause similar symptoms. Trickiest is depression, which can appear to be very like dementia in some people.

A thorough diagnosis will always include a good history which will, among other things, establish the speed of onset. Dementia is usually characterised by a slow onset. Occasionally it starts quickly with multi-infarct dementia. Words like confusion should, in my opinion, be avoided because there are so many causes of confusion and people sometimes think it is synonymous with dementia.

Table 2 summarises the difference between dementia, acute confusional state and depression. A series of guides providing basic information for professionals is available from the Dementia Services Development Centre (see useful addresses at the back of the book). The series includes guides for GPs, community nurses, social workers and occupational therapists.

Stages of dementia have been identified and can be a useful starting point. But they must not be treated as gospel. It is like the concept of stages in the grieving process: useful to know about, but everyone's experience is different. Some people have the stages of dementia to different degrees, some miss stages out. For many people the stages go back and forth.

There are lots of versions of the stages of dementia. The one listed in Table 3 (see next page) is from the invaluable textbook by Jacques (1992) who based it loosely on Hughes et al (1982).

The label "dementia" is, by itself, not very useful as an indicator of the kind of help people need. It often leads to very negative consequences, since people with this label are thought to be mentally incompetent in every respect. It means little without more information about remaining competence, behaviour and physical health, for example. Assessments need to cover a wide range of factors, as described in Chapter 3.

The stages of dementia (loosely based on Hughes C P *et al* 1982 British Journal of Psychiatry 140, 566)	
Healthy	No memory loss, orientated, solves problems, has outside interests, independent in home and in self-care.
Questionable dementia	Mild forgetfulness, but orientated, doubtful impairment of problem-solving and general interest outside and inside the home, independent in self-care.
Mild dementia	Moderate recent memory loss affecting daily life, some disorientation in time, may be disorientated in place in strange surroundings, difficulty handling any complex problems, cannot maintain outside interests, abandons complicated tasks at home, needs some prompting in self-care.
Moderate dementia	Severe memory loss, retains only highly learnt material, disorientated in time and often in place, cannot handle problems or make judgements, unable to function independently away from home, only does the simplest chores at home, needs some assistance in dressing, hygiene, etc.
Severe dementia	Severe memory loss, fragmentary mental activity, completely disorientated except to own identity, unable to solve any problems or make judgements, unable to care for self or to function at home or outside, often incontinent.

Table 3
Table 3 is reproduced from Jacques A (1992) *Understanding Dementia* by the kind permission of Churchill Livingstone.

Service trends
As I said in the Introduction, we work in complex and ever-changing organisations, which themselves operate in a complex and ever-changing society. At the moment, community care is on everyone's lips and yet we have always had community care. We are merely now attempting to care for people in the community who would previously have been in longstay care. To a considerable extent this means shifting limited resources to those in greatest need rather than

providing a reduced amount for larger numbers in less need. Over the years, policies towards care in the community and policies which favour caring for people in institutions have swung to and fro like a pendulum. At the moment the pendulum is swinging towards care outside institutions, but it will swing back again because we need both and finding the right balance is very difficult. Many policies are cost driven. Once the full cost of community care is clarified then the pendulum will undoubtedly swing towards longstay care again. Other policies are scandal driven. There will be horrifying cases of neglect in the community which will support the arguments for longstay care. It could be argued that we are not actually seeing care in the community to any really significant extent. We are instead seeing care in smaller (and not always much smaller) institutions run by private and voluntary organisations rather than the NHS and where charges are made to the individuals receiving care.

It will always be a struggle to get enough resources and enough commitment into this field of care which is why those who choose to work in it must be ready for a fight. People with dementia need strong staff who really believe that they are deserving of the same quality of care as any other citizen.

The pendulum is, at the moment, still swinging away from institutional care, partly as a way of shifting the burden of cost from the public to the personal purse. We are also in a phase of severe demarcation between services as each one tries to shift costs elsewhere. The way we organise services was never suitable for people with dementia. Separating health and welfare for example may make sense for the acute sector. It makes no sense to people with chronic or progressive conditions. They have health and welfare needs which are inextricably intertwined.

It may be helpful to see different professional groups as tribes with their own language, culture, traditions and history. Their relationships are thus, to an extent, characterised by competition, mistrust and power seeking. The big caring organisations are led by the different professional groups. People with dementia and their carers can be the battleground between them. When this happens they are tossed back and forth between the professionals and the organisations, neither side able to offer the seamless, responsive service which adapts to meet their needs.

Much recent social policy is about reducing the power of any one organisation or profession by splitting it into purchasers and providers and by introducing new tribes such as the private sector and the voluntary sector. Having a greater range of purchasers or providers (pluralism) makes the battle lines more complicated but no easier for people with dementia and their carers.

The NHS and Community Care Act (1990) places responsibility for assessment and care management with the local authority. The care manager is the person who helps the person with dementia and their carer to get the best out of the system. The current emphasis on "needs led" assessment will, in theory, mean that the person with dementia and their carer will get a full assessment of need and a package of care will be organised. Inevitably a financial assessment accompanies the needs-led assessment.

If we accept the notion of tribalism, it would explain the fact that the care manager, who in Britain is a welfare professional, is usually able to achieve a care package only in the welfare field. Care packages are seldom drawn up with health and welfare services firmly meshed. At the very least, a team of people, or at least one from each "tribe", is needed in the planning of care. And indeed, this does happen in many psychogeriatric services, but here very dedicated staff tussle with the bureaucracies and the financial regulations to achieve the outcome. It also happens in Australia, where Aged Care Assessment Teams take an interdisciplinary approach to organising individual care.

Miss Harris illustrates a common problem of receiving the unco-ordinated attention of two organisations. She had mild dementia and lived on her own. Neighbours alerted the social work department on one occasion when Miss Harris was very distressed. The GP was called out separately by a visiting nephew. The social worker visited several times in order to make an assessment. Miss Harris refused all offers of help. At the same time, the consultant psychiatrist visited, prescribed medication and mobilised his CPN. Miss Harris quite enjoyed the visits although she had no idea who was who. Each service gave up on her although they were called in at a later date (see Assessment section). Had they known the other service was visiting, they might have got together to discuss Miss Harris and they might have realised that she would have preferred female rather than male visitors (the GP, the psychiatrist, the social worker and the CPN were all men). They could also have usefully shared information about the neighbours who were the main carers.

Finance

Dementia is an expensive business. If the person with dementia has been working, this cannot usually continue. If the carer has been working, this can rarely continue. Most services do not cover a working day, nor can they be guaranteed to be absolutely reliable in terms of time and cover for staff sickness. Many services are not able to cope with the person with dementia's illnesses and bad days. For the working carer, this means that promotion prospects are lost as are pension entitlements, although the invalid care allowance does pay national insurance.

The minority with plenty of money can sometimes buy in assistance; those with little or no money will have to go through financial assessments and claiming. All the time, welfare benefits are diminishing. The independent living scheme, for example, used to be available regardless of age: no longer.

All local authorities now have to make a financial assessment for services, whether provided by them or other agencies which they are using. There are a lot of injustices to be ironed out in the way charges are administered. There is, for example, wide variation in the way that occupational pensions and owned homes are treated. This is particularly worrying for longstay care, where charges are likely to go on for a considerable time. In many respects, it is easier if you have no assets or savings and the local authority has to pay. Staff in all agencies will have to help people cope with the intrusion into their financial affairs, which are often felt to be very private. Staff administering these financial assessments will have to learn how to do it in a way that allows dignity and ensures privacy. We will undoubtedly see sharp practice as the reality of this sinks home and people try to dispose of their assets.

Charges are a nightmare when the person has dementia. Their grasp of their finances is likely to be unreliable, so asking them to sign financial agreements may sometimes be legally dubious. Formal procedures for the management of assets (Curator Bonis in Scotland, Court of Protection in England and Wales, Office of Care and Protection in Northern Ireland) will be required. Some relatives will be watching out for their inheritance and will be unwilling to sanction the payment of services needed. In this country, there is little that can be done about this if the relative has enduring Power of Attorney (explained in the section on the law). In Victoria, Australia, the Office of the Public Advocate can be called in to investigate any circumstances where it seems that a vulnerable person is at risk and this includes financial abuse. Langan and Means (1995) have undertaken some useful research on the issues of personal finance, dementia and community care. They point out that there is a great deal of muddle and misunderstanding which needs to be addressed urgently by local authorities as the lead agencies. Their report is very helpful in fully clarifying the issues.

The welfare benefits world is difficult in a different way. Carers have to take a deep breath and apply, and be ready to appeal. They may need help and support to stick with this especially if they have had a refusal in the past. People with dementia may need quite a lot of help to understand. Often it is necessary to find someone they trust to help them. People who are losing their memories can become very anxious and suspicious, presumably because they know they are not in full control of their lives any more. Helping people claim is dealt with more fully in Chapter 3.

Housing

People with dementia and their carers will be in every kind of housing and each one has its advantages and disadvantages.

The home owner in a detached house will have the advantage of being able to take more risks than the person in a flat who can cause consternation to neighbours who imagine the flat burning down. Sheltered housing has the advantage of a warden, but this can also feel like a disadvantage to the person with dementia because it can mean that action, such as removal, is taken faster as competence diminishes and if behaviour is unacceptable in these quasicommunal settings.

From the point of view of those with dementia, a familiar house is a huge advantage. Their learning ability is very impaired and they often fail to adjust to a new place. It is often a mistake for persons with dementia to move closer to relatives because they have to learn not only a new house but new faces and a new community.

Having said this, some new housing options are very attractive, combining as they do a small, domestic setting and care. There is a unit in Glasgow, for example, built by a housing association as part of a street of their houses, financed by the health board and the social work department and managed by a charity. Eight people with dementia live in this housing, as far as possible doing the chores and everyday tasks such as going to the post office or betting shop. It is registered as a residential home. "Very sheltered housing" and "extra care housing" are two terms for this emerging model of housing plus care. There are, as yet, no evaluations available, but there do seem to be some benefits from this kind of housing for people who cannot remain in their own homes.

This may be related to the issue of size. Research which compares small, domestic style units with longstay wards always shows that the former aid orientation and self-care: Lindesay et al (1991), for example. The line between housing and residential care is very hazy with these units.

Although design is dealt with in a later chapter, it is worth mentioning here that the concept of barrier-free housing is slowly being extended to include design to minimise disorientation (Martin 1992). The idea of barrier-free design is that every house should be able to accommodate a degree of disability since such a house will also be better for people who are pregnant, pushing prams, injured or sick. The same applies to disorientation. We can design houses so that the layout is more easily understood. We should try and do this because there will be times when all of us experience disorientation if we are stressed or ill. It is more difficult to make an existing house "make sense", but not impossible. Most bathrooms of the 1940s had a glazed door for example: it is only recently that bathroom doors have been made to look the same as any other. So a house might usefully be adapted in this way so the person with dementia can find the bathroom independently.

The law

There are two kinds of law especially relevant to the care of people with dementia and their carers: the law relating to the proper care of people with dementia and the law relating to their property and assets.

Use of the law in relation to the care of people with dementia is about how you achieve a balance between civil liberty and proper protection. There are no easy answers. How do you decide when you are unreasonably restricting someone like Mr Sexton, for example? He was a big, energetic man who walked constantly, often getting lost and having to be brought home by the police. His wife, who was a good deal less fit than he was, walked with him until she was exhausted. She then resorted to locking the front door and pretending she had lost the key. He became very aggressive and restless. The day centre could not manage him either. They felt unhappy at having to lock their door which restricted the other members. The day hospital was only able to keep Mr Sexton for assessment and diagnosis. Mrs Sexton became ill, probably through stress, and Mr Sexton was admitted to a nursing home where they have a bolt high up on the front door and all the other doors have buzzers on them. He made it very clear that he resented this restriction on his liberty, often becoming very angry. Seldom does he get very far, although he seems to have wings on his feet when he does get out. Staff try and take him for walks and outings whenever they can. The nursing home is in another town, so he would never be able to find his way back to either his home or the nursing home. How are we to achieve a balance between Mr Sexton's civil liberties and the need to protect him from harm?

Contrast Mr Sexton with Mrs Lauder who had always lived at the same end of a small town as the old people's home where she was a resident. She was always able to find her way back or be helped by locals who knew her. The degree of independent decision-making allowed is a question of judgement. Another contrast is with Mr Deans who is the kind of example more often quoted because he represents the most feared outcome of the policy of leaving the door open. He left his old people's home and was found dead the following day.

Staff have a duty of care, so if a case ended up in court they would have to show they had taken this seriously. This would generally be shown by examination of records as well as interviews with staff. Records are referred to in more length in Chapter 3. Staff would also have to show that unreasonable restrictions were not in force, that alternative approaches had been attempted and that decisions were made in a responsible way. It is not easy but the actual legislation is rarely invoked.

Assisting with the making of difficult decisions on when to detain people is the daily bread and butter of Mental Health Officers and a discussion with them is always useful. What is not useful is taking the stand which says that people with dementia should never be subject to the mental health legislation. There is a curious ageism about this. Many staff are unwilling to put the time and effort required into considering the mental health legislation for an older person whereas they would not hesitate for a younger person at similar risk. Whereas much of the mental health legislation is about formally detaining people in hospital, there is the mechanism of Guardianship. This is when a Guardian (usually the local authority), who has the power to decide where the person with dementia shall live, making her attend for treatment, occupation, education or training and ensuring access to her by a doctor or other such person, is appointed. The Guardian cannot consent to medical treatment or make decisions about finances.

An aside here about the legal position of relatives. In practice, relatives make a lot of decisions on behalf of the person with dementia. Staff consult them all the time. Generally speaking this is entirely appropriate since they have the best interests of the person at heart. However, we all need to be on the alert for occasions when there is a conflict of interest, and to bear in mind that, strictly speaking, relatives cannot legally decide on behalf of the person with dementia. Guardianship can be appropriate to help with the Mr Sextons of this world, not least because it brings experienced minds to bear upon worries about Mr Sexton. There are proper safe-guards to Guardianship and it means that no individual has to make the decision to restrict his civil liberties themselves. There may be occasions where someone like Mr Sexton needs to be the subject of a mental health section because he is a danger to himself and/or others; indeed, had the situation at home continued this would probably have been the case.

The mental health legislation is different in England and Wales, Scotland and Northern Ireland, but the basic principles and approach should be the same. The legislation exists to make exactly the difficult judgements about civil liberty versus protection with which many staff are wrestling.

Other types of legislation are about property and assets. An Appointee can be created by the Secretary of State to act on behalf of DSS claimants who cannot manage their affairs. The Appointee applies in writing and social security staff need to check that people with dementia cannot manage their own affairs. They usually do this by requesting a letter from a doctor. They also usually visit the person applying to be the Appointee and the person with dementia. It is worth thinking very carefully before applying because the responsibility of being an Appointee is considerable. It is, for example, not usually a good idea for the manager of a private or voluntary home to be an Appointee.

Power of Attorney empowers someone to make decisions on behalf of someone else, but lapses if the person giving it becomes mentally incompetent. Enduring Power of Attorney carries on, but must be given before the person becomes incompetent. It is no use suddenly realising that people with dementia are unable to manage their money and then trying to organise Power of Attorney. Court of Protection (England and Wales), Office of Care and Protection (Northern Ireland) and Curator Bonis (Scotland) are all about looking after property and assets when someone is incompetent. They are not really appropriate unless there are substantial assets because they involve complex legal procedures and there are costs incurred.

One of the problems with United Kingdom legislation is that you are either wholly incompetent or wholly competent in the law, whereas many people with dementia remain able to decide about some aspects of their lives but not about others. Mr Sexton, for example, could tell his wife that he wanted his money left to his daughter but was nevertheless unable to stop himself walking out of the home and getting lost. The Law Commissions of both England and Wales and Scotland are addressing this issue at present.

Physical health
The importance of maintaining as good physical health as possible cannot be over-estimated. People with dementia are struggling to cope with the world and anything which lowers their potential functioning should be minimised. Given that dementia is most common in old people aged over eighty, there are likely to be the multiple disabilities and illnesses that occur in this age group. Arthritis is common, as is heart malfunction. Chest conditions are relatively common too. Equally disabling are foot problems. Cutting long toenails, for example, can make an astonishing difference to morale and mobility. Treating constipation can also make a huge difference to intellectual function and well-being. Eyesight and hearing

impairments are often missed or attributed to the failing brain. One of the difficulties is that the person with dementia is not able to explain where it hurts, how it hurts and whether they have a history of a certain condition. There is often a degree of malnutrition for various reasons which will be dealt with in due course.

All the usual homilies about a good diet, regular exercise and plenty of sleep apply to people with dementia. However, workers need to be extra vigilant about physical health. Is the skin tone good? Are the eyes sparkling? Is the posture uncomfortable? Is walking painful? and so on. Medication is a special issue when working with people who cannot always be relied upon to take it correctly and when the side-effects can sometimes exacerbate disorientation. Mixing over-the-counter with prescribed medicines is a frequent hazard.

Personhood
This may seem an odd section to put in a book which aims throughout to emphasise the need to see people with dementia as individuals. But this approach needs to be spelled out. As Kitwood and Bredin (1992) say in their eloquent book *Person to Person*:

> *"When we really appreciate that each person is special, a new window is opened on the task of caring. We see how vital it is to take account of the unique desires, tastes, abilities, difficulties and fears of the one we are looking after. And we need to remember that any or all of these may change as time goes on. It isn't easy, of course, and there have to be compromises. There are many things we simply have to get done, in order to carry on from day to day" (p 17).*

Working to safeguard the personhood, the specialness, of the person with dementia is the responsibility of all of us working with people with dementia. There are some issues that throw this challenge into sharp relief. One is sex. Imagining that people with dementia are sexual beings is sometimes really difficult. Sex and dementia are generally assumed to be about the sexually disinhibited behaviour of some people with dementia. This is not an easy issue in itself, but it is immeasurably more difficult if we have not come to terms with the possibility of people with dementia having sexual needs. First we need to be able to talk about sex. This requires a shared language to diminish the embarrassment and it may require practice. Then we need to be able to see sexually disinhibited behaviour as an effort to communicate something: we need to understand the reasons for it. But this is only one dimension. Another is that people with dementia may want a sexual relationship: homosexual or heterosexual. They may also be scarred by sexual abuse at some time in their lives. The pain may come to the surface as the defences become less successful.

Another recognition of personhood comes with the recognition of the spiritual needs of people with dementia. This may mean a need for worship in whatever faith they have practised. It may mean time and opportunity for meditation and reflection. It may be in the attention to music or to the countryside. It is invariably in peace and quiet, which can be a rare occurrence in many settings. Some people need company for spiritual journeys, others like to be alone.

A third issue of personhood is in the confrontation of death and bereavement. Most of us find this extremely difficult yet settings where death and bereavement are topics of normal conversation report that they are popular topics and that people with dementia derive great comfort in being allowed and enabled to talk about them. Many older people want to be able to talk about sex and death but are sensitive to the taboos that make it impossible with family and friends. We can provide these opportunities, if we ourselves are able to cope.

Abuse
Abuse is more than violence against people with dementia. It includes psychological abuse, deprivation, forcible isolation, misusing medication and misusing moneys and property (BASW 1990). It includes any unwelcome or non-agreed intrusion. Thus it includes sexual behaviour if this is not welcome. Working out when people with dementia are, or are not, consenting to sex is one of the issues addressed in Archibald's (1994) useful video and training materials.

Many carers will admit to rough treatment of the person with dementia they are caring for. Many will tell you that they themselves have been the victims of rough treatment by the person with dementia. This is understandable if not acceptable and is usually not more than an isolated occurrence.

Sometimes, however, there is a pattern of physical mistreatment. It would seem from the research that this seldom occurs in isolation and usually occurs in families where there is a history of violence. It is often combined with disturbed relationships, poverty and alcoholism. Dementia is only one factor, albeit a powerful one. Whether or not this is also the case with other kinds of abuse is less clear. It seems likely that it would be the case with sexual abuse. It seems unlikely to have started in old age, although of course there are very disturbed people outside the family who get a thrill from molesting old people.

Financial abuse is another matter and must be the most common form of abuse against people with dementia. It seems likely that many people financially abuse people with dementia who can be persuaded to hand over the responsibility for their finances and are unable to check what happens. It is just so easy. Neglect is another form of abuse, which can have many contributory factors such as ignorance, lack of skills, depression and so on. Finally, abuse may happen in a concealed way through medication. Relatives may dose the person with dementia into a torpor to give themselves some peace.

Many local authorities now have guidelines for their staff. Pritchard (1992) provides examples from three local authorities. They are very helpful in listing factors which make abuse likely, and guidance on suspicious signs and symptoms, as well as procedures for action.

Abuse is not merely a family issue as some of the residential home scandals have demonstrated. In these homes, physical abuse is as common as psychological abuse. Some of the standards that have existed in longstay care amount to abuse: standards that would never be condoned with more articulate residents and patients. Residents are undoubtedly sexually abused by staff from time to time and financial abuse is not unusual. The untrained care staff in The Pines Nursing Home were appalled to see their new unit manager apparently fondling the breasts of the women residents when they were in bed. He claimed he was checking for breast cancer but this plainly did not need to be done as often as he was doing it. The staff reported the matter to the manager of the home who was having great difficulty recruiting staff to run his dementia unit and was unwilling to take any action. The staff were not convinced he thought it was very important anyway. They felt defeated because they had no idea who to go to in order to complain and they were not sure that anyone else would believe them. It was their word as a group of untrained staff against the trained staff.

Complaining about care is difficult. The correct route is through the levels of management. Many organisations have procedures in place for internal complaints. Staff in the private and voluntary sector are usually encouraged to go through the levels of management and, if this is not successful, to the registration sections, who will not divulge the source of the complaint.

However, management of longstay care units and even registration sections do not always have up-to-date ideas about dementia care. Many staff in senior positions were trained on longstay wards when the prevailing belief was that people with dementia were so neurologically damaged that they had no feelings as well as no understanding. Only ten years ago this was a view regularly voiced in the wards of a very poor longstay hospital I worked in. Beds were pushed together in thirty bedded Nightingale wards to make day spaces at the end of them in which patients either sat slumped in chairs or wandered aimlessly about for hours at a time banging into each other or periodically shaking the door. Almost all the clothes were identical hospital issue. Meal times were like the monkey house at the zoo. Staff seemed to have no understanding of how inhumane these conditions were. They pointed out that the patients were clean, dressed and fed. Relatives consoled themselves and me with assurances that it was just as well the people with dementia had no idea about the care they received. . . . We all knew I think, though we never said, that the patients still had feelings and that we would not keep our cat in such places. The guilt feelings of the relatives were agonising, but in every case they had cared at home at great personal expense until it became quite impossible to continue. Staff who were trained in these environments will often fail to see people with dementia as people with feelings.

Some staff are driven, perhaps sometimes too soon, to the media. There are often alternatives. There are many local special interest groups. In my experience they are often very effective problem-solving groups where there are people with contacts and influence who can work in various indirect ways to improve standards. Local Alzheimer's Disease Society branches often have connections into officialdom and are willing to conceal the source of their information. Professional associations and trade unions can be very skilful at taking cases discreetly to the highest authorities.

There are big problems of whistle blowing, by which I mean formally complaining about standards and if necessary going to the Press. Sometimes the standards are not so much scandalous as just poor. I visit a lot of places and I consider standards sometimes to be thoroughly mediocre or not good enough, but they are not actually really bad. Sometimes it is impossible to get evidence as in the case of The Pines above. There is a campaign group (Freedom to Care) which believes that whistle blowing represents a moral and ethical assertion of one's citizenship. They are pressing for legislation. Their address is in the appendix. Whistle blowers do seem to suffer greatly from their colleagues and often from their employers. Some people believe that they have been blacklisted for whistle blowing although there is rarely any evidence for this. It is worthwhile working very hard to find a constructive way to influence standards before taking formal action and to complain with a group of colleagues where possible rather than alone.

Restraint

Following a section on abuse with one on restraint is not an accident. Much restraint is no different from abuse, but a line has to be drawn between the carefully monitored and recorded restraint and the thoughtless depriving of liberty. Any action which restrains someone, whether it be through medication, being confined to a chair, being confined behind a locked door or constrained by a bewildering gate must not be undertaken lightly and can only be justified if it is the absolute minimum necessary. The duty to protect tends to be uppermost in people's minds in these circumstances, but sometimes it is the protection of staff's backs which is the primary concern. This should not surprise us given the hunt for scapegoats whenever anything goes wrong. Staff need to know what the limits are when they allow the residents to take risks. They also need to know that there are channels of communication should they feel that there is either too much restraint or careless risk-taking. Good practice with restraint means recording the following each time it is used:

● What is the problem and why is it a problem?

● What other methods have been tried to deal with this problem?

● Details of the full discussion with relatives and other key people in the person's life (advocacy may need to be considered for people without relatives and friends).

● What decision was made about the restraint to be used and by whom?

● Firm time limits specified.

● Specified time for review and who will be involved.

One of the main issues is wandering. This is not a very accurate term for the often quite purposeful behaviour of people with dementia. They are usually not able to say why they are walking so it is necessary for staff to look for their reasons. In Table 4, Allan (1994) has provided a checklist of possible reasons.

Table 4

CHECKLIST - WHY DO PEOPLE WITH DEMENTIA WANDER?

Possible reasons

- Continuation of lifestyle patterns:
  occupation
  leisure
  response to stress

- Neurological damage

- Anxiety/sadness/anger

- Boredom

- Need for toilet

- Pain

- Other physical/psychiatric illness

- Loss of navigational skills

- Faulty goal-directed behaviour

- Need for exercise

- Form of communication

- Medication side effects

- Desire to leave (!)

Table 4 is reproduced from Allan K (Ed) Wandering published by the Dementia Services Development Centre.

Working out why is a major step in trying to do something about it. It still may not be possible to allow such people to walk away if there is some danger of a busy road or bad weather. However, restraining someone because they want to walk should be a decision made very carefully. It can be utterly exhausting for carers to have to accompany someone who wants to walk a lot and it may be necessary to find an alternative way of giving the person with dementia enough exercise, without wearing out their relative, such as a volunteer who enjoys walking.

Mr Jepson was a terrible nuisance, even a hazard, on the acute medical ward where he was receiving treatment for his kidney condition. He was on the move all the time and was constantly getting underfoot or vanishing from the ward. It transpired that he was a very active man at home and that he and his wife spent a lot of time walking. Staff agreed amongst themselves that whoever had to go to another part of the hospital, for some reason, took him with them. He was not a well man and this degree of exercise meant he was pleased to settle down in a chair when he got back to the ward.

The need to walk affects a lot of people with dementia and it is sad to find so many day centres and longstay units without good, safe outdoor space with plenty of distractions. Given a well-designed environment and enough planned activity, it seems that wandering can be eliminated in longstay care. Nancy Peppard (1991), who runs a consultancy in the USA for longstay care for people with dementia, claims that wandering is a myth.

Dilemmas

It is no use pretending that there are always right answers. Judgement is required all the time. Risk was touched on in the previous chapter and is fraught with dilemmas. How much risk should we allow the person with dementia to take, given that they are often unable to work out the consequences. The line between allowing someone to be independent and to try to do things and simply allowing them to fail is not a clear one. Failure is every bit as bad an outcome as hurting themselves. Having dementia is all about failure in every aspect of life, which leads to loss of confidence, low morale and great anxiety. We have to do every-thing we can to reduce the sense of failure. Activities should be failure-free as far as possible. Fine judgements are therefore required to allow enough calculated risk for the person with dementia to be able to succeed at something with enough pro-tection to ensure there is neither failure nor injury of some sort. Perhaps the occasional injury is a fair price to pay for some independence and success: but this should be seen as not an abdication of responsibility but rather a careful judgement.

Mr di Rollo illustrates a considered approach to risk taking. He had had dementia for many years and was no longer able to speak properly. He was constantly near tears and constantly plucking at his clothes and the clothes of people near him. He was very shaky. He seemed unable to relate to anybody. His day centre used the preparation of the lunch as its main activity. The staff knew that Mr di Rollo had been an experienced chef and that some of his skills remained. His hands were washed, a chopping board was placed in front of him, upon which was placed a large potato that had been peeled by one of the other members, and into his right hand was placed a razor-sharp chopping knife. Mr di Rollo sliced the potato for the soup with no hesitation, placing the knife on the board when he had finished. Effusive thanks and approval were his reward.

Another recurring dilemma is the needs of the individual versus the needs of the group. Inevitably we are often involved in group care. This book takes as a starting point that the needs of the individual are paramount, but we have to recognise that this cannot always be so. How do we weigh up the welfare of a group of residents unable to go outside when they want to because one resident makes off if allowed through the door? How do we weigh up the welfare of a group of residents denied access to their bedrooms because another resident cannot resist ferreting through the dressing table drawers? A lot of this, again, is about behaviour management and this book should give extensive ideas on this if nothing else. But it would be foolish to pretend that there is not a continuous tension and constant difficult decisions to be made, even when each individual has a care plan and these are being consistently implemented by all the staff.

Another dilemma is the extent to which carers can legitimately speak on behalf of the person with dementia. Most people with dementia need an advocate because they are unable to speak on their own behalf. Who better than someone who knows them really well? But it is not always in the interests of the person with dementia. Indeed, there are sometimes quite sharp conflicts of interest and these are one of the reasons why work in this field is so very difficult. It used to be much easier when we believed that people with dementia had no meaningful preferences. Now we know that they have, we have to face the fact that it is often excruciatingly difficult to see a fair solution.

Table 5

EARLY STAGES	
Carers' needs and demands	**People with dementia's needs and demands**
information	information
counselling	counselling
a social life	a social life

MIDDLE STAGES	
Carers' needs and demands	**People with dementia's needs and demands**
breaks	familiar places
normal social life	familiar people
shared care	individual care
peace of mind, rest	taking risks/organised stimulation
recognition	lots of unconditional warmth
training	someone to talk to
someone to talk to	others to take responsibility
practical help	

END STAGES	
Carers' needs and demands	**People with dementia's needs and demands**
to relinquish all or much	familiar places
twenty-four-hour care	familiar people
	individual care
counselling	good physical care
self-esteem	stimulation
	unconditional warmth

Table 5 illustrates this point by looking at some of the conflicts of interests between the needs of people with dementia and their carers. It is full of generalisations but some recognisable tensions are there between, for example, the need for breaks for the carer and the necessity to have a constant familiar carer for the person with dementia.

Although dementia is primarily a disease of old age, younger people do get it and their families often illustrate the most difficult conflicts of interest. Mr Shaw and his wife were both lawyers who married late and had a young family even though they were in their late forties. They both worked and were very successful until Mr Shaw got dementia. He gave up work, though not willingly. Mrs Shaw was very unwilling to give up her successful career: she was the main breadwinner but the only person who could keep her husband calm and relaxed. The children were very distressed by their father's behaviour. The conflict of interests was very painful. Mr Shaw needed to be with his wife all the time but Mrs Shaw needed and wanted to work. The children might well have been less stressed had their father been in hospital.

One way of working towards a solution which is fair even if it does not fully meet the needs of either party is the one used by trade unions and diplomats: negotiation. This is a process where each party specifies what it wants and then works towards an agreed compromise where it is felt that concessions on both sides have been fair. In family situations, both sides may need to be represented; certainly the person with dementia will need this. It will not be a process to be used very often, but for some of the really difficult ones it may be the way forward. Mediation is another related technique used by the family conciliation service, who work with divorcing couples. With mediation, both parties are helped to put their case fully to the other. The tensions between carers and people with dementia have all the emotional components of any marriage, even when they are not married to each other. In many situations there are several staff involved who might undertake the roles of negotiators or mediators. The social worker might assist the person with dementia, and the CPN assist the carer in the case of Mr and Mrs Shaw, for example.

Chapter 3
Communication

Communication with people with dementia

This is perhaps the most exciting area of development in the field at present. We are slowly learning that it is possible to communicate with people with dementia although we still have a lot to learn. Enabling them to share their wishes and preferences with us is perhaps the most urgent need but increasingly the possibility of therapeutic communication is being recognised.

People in the early stages of the illness will often be able to communicate verbally. What is needed is skill in listening which allow them to ask and to share whatever they want and need. This can be very stressful for both us and them because they will be grappling with making sense of a life with a progressive illness. It is impossible to generalise about what people in this position will want to communicate. It may be reviewing their life, it may be planning their future. They will want different amounts of information, and will have different worries.Some people in the early stages will want to know their diagnosis, others will not. It can be helpful for a diagnosis to be shared with the person and their family at the same time.

When carers are told about the diagnosis, and the person with dementia is not told, it can put a great strain on relationships and can isolate the person with dementia yet further. Mr Fields would, from time to time, ask his daughter if there was something wrong with his head. She found this acutely stressful because the doctors had only spoken to relatives and not to Mr Fields about the diagnosis. She felt neither competent nor comfortable about being the person to tell her father about the diagnosis. As a consequence a barrier was erected between them and he was left alone with his fears.

It is not easy for the doctors to decide how, when and with whom to share the diagnosis and they often fall back on their own preferences. It would seem to be good practice, at least in the early stages, to assume the person with dementia wants some information and to take it in tiny steps, providing only what they seem to want to know, much in the way that telling about cancer is approached. Mr Crerar lived in sheltered housing with his wife. The warden seemed to be the one person in Mr Crerar's life who did not shy away from discussing his diminishing competence with him. He was able to share his knowledge that he had dementia and the fact that he was very fearful of the future. It was a great comfort to him. The warden never used the word "dementia". Neither did she confront him with explanations. She simply listened, gave no false reassurances and told no lies.

It is often helpful to start with the assumption that people in the middle and later stages of dementia communicate symbolically and emotionally. They are seldom able to explain in plain, straightforward language what it is they want to tell you. This does not mean they never can, but often they cannot tell you at the time you want to hear. Mr Mackie, for example, was able to tell his daughter exactly what he had disliked about the day centre he had attended, but only six months after when he was happily settled in an old people's home. Mrs Turner's key worker thought Mrs Turner lived in about four time zones, one of which was the present. When she was in the present it was quite possible to have a straightforward conversation with her.

It is always best to assume that people with dementia can express preferences or make choices in a straightforward verbal fashion. It may, however, be necessary to choose the right moment and spend a bit of time engaging the person. It may be necessary to speak their first language or dialect.

More complicated conversations are possible but require time and skill. Time is often the key. John Killick, who provided the poem which prefaces this book, is employed by a nursing home company as Writer in Residence. He spends hours talking to the residents and they are able to tell him something about what it feels like to have dementia, as did the woman who said: "I've lost my personality this morning, I hope it comes back this afternoon." He maintains that by positioning yourself correctly and concentrating very hard, it is possible to establish a rapport with many people in the later stages of the disease.

Staff in day hospitals and longstay units say that many of the best conversations take place in the bathroom with the warm water and pleasant smells encouraging easy communication. Seeing bathing as therapeutic as well as hygienic can have very positive outcomes for people with dementia and can give staff great job satisfaction.

Language can be a problem. The dementia often means that the second language is lost. Mr Singh, for example, was unable to communicate with his grandchildren, in spite of the fact that they were at home with him to a far greater extent than his son and daughter-in-law who worked very long hours in their grocery shop. The grandchildren spoke no Punjabi.

In my view, we are increasingly realising that people with dementia are trying to communicate in whatever way they can. Sometimes they tell us apparently unconnected stories, often about their past. Sometimes they have only behaviour as a means of communicating. If we start with this premise we may begin to be able to "listen". In other words, we have to assume a rationality about their conversation and their behaviour rather than irrationality as we have in the past.

Why is it that Mrs Casson endlessly tells us about her brother's death? Could she perhaps be wanting to talk about death? A day centre in Geelong which actively encourages the expression of feelings finds that attenders talk a lot about death. It is certainly true that social workers working with old people generally find that sex and death are two topics many older people want to talk about because they are not able to share these thoughts with their relatives and friends. Mrs Casson needs a listener who will let her talk. She may simply be saying that she is miserable. Naomi Feil (1992), the originator of Validation Therapy, believes that people reach old age with a lot of unfinished emotional business and that, as the defences weaken as a result of dementia, this unfinished business comes to the surface. She claims that relief can be given to the person with dementia through what she calls "exquisite listening" and through help in expressing the emotion. In Mrs Casson's case it might be helpful to say: "Tell me about your brother. Was his death especially painful for you?" Staying with the feelings, Feil (1992) maintains, helps people to express them and, once expressed, they are in some way dealt with. We all know how good it is to talk and unburden ourselves when we are unhappy about something. Whether or not one believes that a resolution can be found (and this approach is sometimes called "resolution therapy"), really attentive observation and listening for the feelings behind the story must be helpful and beneficial.

If we look at the behaviour of people with dementia with knowledge and experience of them we can sometimes act as interpreters. Why is it that Mr Allan, for example, will sometimes only pick at his food and leaves most of it, causing his wife considerable distress and anxiety, whereas at other times he eats it all? If you watch Mr Allan it is clear that when he is agitated for some reason he is unable to eat. He also uses it as a way of expressing anger with his wife which he cannot express verbally because he is only too well aware that he is totally dependent on her. If you talk to her, you realise that she expresses a lot of love and care through food and she feels his behaviour to be very rejecting of her. Meal times can easily become a battleground. Mrs Baxter spits her food out in her old people's home, causing immense mess and consternation. Is she expressing her rage and impotence at her predicament? Mrs Hughes stopped eating at all unless she was fed like a baby in her nursing home. It seemed that this started after she had realised that her husband was dead. This realisation had taken some weeks - she seemed surprisingly unconcerned at the time. Once she had voiced the fact that he was dead, she stopped eating. She now needs to be hugged like a baby and fed soft foods with a spoon, often weeping. She is very fortunate to be in a nursing home where they are willing to give her this kind of care, because it can take an hour to spoon the bowl of mashed food into her mouth.

It may be that the common preoccupation with babies is a way some people with dementia have of telling us that they long for the physical warmth and closeness a baby brings. Mrs White's key worker had been trying for some weeks to get Mrs White to explain more about the baby she kept talking about. The incessant talking stopped when the worker simply hugged Mrs White and stroked her hand.

Perhaps we can interpret some behaviour of people with dementia as attempts to make sense of the bewildering situations in which they find themselves. Mr Leith was in an acute hospital ward. He was sitting in a chair with a wheeled bedside table across his knees to stop him getting up because he had a drip in his arm. He seemed convinced that the table was a potato machine that needed fixing. To the dismay of nurses he kept trying to get under it to see what was wrong. The nurses did not have the skills to get him to talk about the machine. He might have been able to express his fears about the fact that something was very wrong with his life through talking about the faulty machine.

In the section on restraint, I suggested that wandering is another kind of behaviour by which people are trying to communicate and the same can be said of any behaviour. Of course, this will not always be the case, but it is worth at the outset assuming that it is. "Hearing" what people with dementia are trying to say to us does not make life any easier because we often then have to do something about it. Is Mr Sexton telling us with his wandering that he wants to escape because he does not like our nursing home? We then have to do something about it if we can. We can teach Mr Allan's wife some relaxation techniques so that she stays calmer around meal times. We can allow Mrs Baxter and Mrs Hughes to express their rage or unhappiness more appropriately or perhaps we can cope better ourselves and not become too overwrought at their behaviour.

Written communications: records
Interpreting the communication of someone with dementia is immeasurably easier if we know something about them. Records are a way of collecting and storing this information and making it available appropriately. Most agencies keep some sort of record of essential information such as addresses of next of kin, essential medical information and so on. Some agencies keep biographical information.

Ideally there ought to be a set of records. Basic and biographical information should be supplemented by information about preferences. In my case, if you did not know that I always slept with the curtains open, you would be risking some very troublesome bedtimes if I had dementia and was unable to tell you.

Preferences are often extraordinarily trivial. Gibson (1991) describes the positive impact of knowing preferences in residential care. When Mrs O'Reilly was dying of cancer, her key worker had the foresight to seek her help in preparing a life-story book about Mr O'Reilly who had dementia. The book also referred to his preferences and included the fact that he loathed striped shirts. Not knowing this might have led to difficult behaviour once Mrs O'Reilly was not there to explain. Information about preferences should be available to those who need to know. There is no point in having information in the office about the fact that Mrs Jones likes to put her knickers and stockings on before her dress. It needs to be in her bedroom. Overton Nursing Home in Melbourne has this kind of information summarised on a sheet inside the wardrobe door.

As in the case of Mr O'Reilly there is often a need for a life-story book (Murphy 1994). This need not, of course, need to be a full life story, rather aspects of life and interests. Some people do not want to share the story of their lives, especially if they are ashamed of them or they have been very traumatic. But what is needed is a book showing what is important to a person. Often it is major life events: work, marriage, children. For others it may be their regiment or football club, their family being of much less consequence. These books give everyone the information they need to relate to that person: staff, relatives and visitors to the unit or to the person at home. They are best if they are full of pictures without too much text although some text is required to make sure the pictures and memorabilia are not misinterpreted. Life-story books as an activity are discussed in Chapter 4.

There is an inbuilt reluctance to complete records. They are often the lowest priority, the last job to do. They are often woefully inadequate. Why is this? I think it is because they are seen as a chore for which there is no clear explanation. If staff understood that they are, in fact, the memory of the person with dementia, they might feel differently. Without a good record of both the past and the present, communicating with people with dementia and organising their care and management cannot be achieved. This is particularly true in longstay settings where there are inevitable shift changes, plus the other staff changes that arise from holidays, sick leave and staff leaving.

Communication with carers

Carers always tell us, if we give them the chance, that they need more information. If there is an early diagnosis then, like the person with dementia, they need as much but not more information about the illness than they can understand and cope with. It is not easy to know what to share because the pathway through the illness is so unpredictable. Mrs Shepherd could not face the full possibilities of the future for her husband when he was first diagnosed. The books and leaflets stayed unread for a long time, but, as she got more accustomed, she read them a little at a time and felt the strength of knowing the worst possible outcome. Many carers simply cannot face the facts at all. Mr Crichton's wife was diagnosed when she was still well able to talk about it. He found this intolerable and refused to acknowledge that she had dementia or to talk to anyone about it. This diagnosis is little different from any diagnosis of a terminal illness.

Some people want to know all the details of their relative's cancer, others prefer to ignore it. The point for us here is that we must be ready to provide the information in as small or large quantities required by the carer. Although medical staff make the diagnosis, it is often the non-medical staff who have to explain it. There are some very helpful leaflets and books now available. The Alzheimer's Disease Society and Alzheimer Scotland - Action on Dementia are finely tuned to the needs of carers, and have a range of materials including videos and can advise on other booklets and books. Carers can often tell you what information they want.

As the disease progresses, carers need to know what help is available. Being able to ask for help is a real skill and one which carers seldom manage effectively without feeling either diminished or angry. It helps if they know where to go and to whom to speak in the first place so that they are not pushed from pillar to post, losing their nerve and their energy as they go. Staff need to know what is available locally. Being alongside a carer through this process is a vital job for front-line staff. Although we sometimes have to speak on their behalf, we can be more helpful if we help them to ask themselves. It is very easy to make distressed carers dependent on us.

Carers do not need false reassurance about the illness and the services. It is up to us to be straight and as honest as we can be. Many are anxious at the beginning about whether they will be able to cope and it can be helpful to emphasise that it is impossible to predict what they will have to cope with. One of the greatest strains is not being able to talk to the person with dementia in an honest way. Some people find that having to pretend that there is nothing wrong is a great strain.

Obviously this will vary from one relationship to another, which is why really careful listening is so important. In some relationships coping without talking about feelings has been their custom, in others they share everything. There can be no rules except the fundamental one of listening very carefully and responding, which, of course, requires skill and good support for staff.

Carers often say that they want to be more involved in the services their relative is receiving, like Mrs Cross. Her husband had been attending the day hospital for a year. She had no idea what went on there. When she asked Mr Cross he said that they took all his clothes off and that he had lunch, he could remember little else. Mrs Cross suggested to the charge nurse that she might attend with him one day but she was energetically discouraged on the basis that this was a day off for her. She was anxious because she felt she knew what was best for her husband and nobody was asking her. She also wanted to be able to continue any treatment he received on the days he was not at the day hospital. Miss Blair is another carer who should have had more information. Miss Blair's mother was in a residential home which she had believed was her mother's home for life. She was very distressed when her mother was suddenly moved to a psychiatric hospital because the home could no longer cope. She said she felt betrayed. If the staff had been honest with her they would have told her that the home would only keep residents as long as they did not disrupt the unit. Her mother had become very aggressive.

Of course it is not always entirely straightforward. Carers may want inappropriate degrees of control. Mr Wheeler's mother had become attracted to one of the male residents and the staff had not shared this with Mr Wheeler because they felt he would not have coped with his mother's sexuality and would have asked the staff to prevent the relationship. This difference of opinion between staff and residents is most common on the issue of risk. Relatives have often come to terms with the idea of longstay care because they feel their relative will be safer. They can be dismayed to find unlocked doors, kitchens and energetic activities. Staff need to be open about their approach and this may even mean talking about risk, sex and death before the admission. A good brochure about the philosophy of care is a useful starting point. Most relatives are not unreasonable people and appreciate a good discussion so they can feel that their relative is going to receive planned care set within a well-considered philosophy.

Mr Deans left his residential home without anybody seeing and his body was found in the river the following day. The relatives were fully aware of the philosophy of the home, and policy of the local authority which included unlocked doors. They also saw that a full investigation was undertaken to check that Mr Deans' departure could not have been prevented. They would not have wanted their father locked in because he would have felt trapped. The media were very interested in this case; a consistent response about unlocked doors was held from the top of the organisation down so there was no story to tell.

Clear, continuing communication is the best basis for a real understanding. A written brochure should be backed up in discussions. Every staff member should be aware of the policies and be willing to talk things through. If there is a difference of opinion about what is best for the person with dementia then it should be out in the open, discussed and some negotiated agreement arrived at. Implicit in all this is the approach of staff to carers, which should always be respectful; carers can be very sensitive to any slight because they frequently feel that receiving help is an implicit criticism. Non-verbal communication is as important as verbal and the rule of thumb is that if people hear something and see something else, they will believe what they see. We say: "We always have time to tell carers what is going on," and they see that when we are talking to them we are constantly answering the phone and speaking to people who come through the door. They will get the message!

Cultural differences can make communication difficult. Mrs Hamid lived with her son and daughter-in-law. Mr Hamid junior was insistent that his wife had a duty to care for his mother and he would not allow any additional help. The younger Mrs Hamid had never liked her mother-in-law and felt desperate to talk and to receive some respite. There was little anyone could do to help her.

One of the best ways to communicate with carers can be in groups and this is covered in greater length in the section on groupwork. Carers' groups are often assumed to be a "good thing", but with little thought given to matching the aims with the type of group. Large meetings will be good for giving information, as long as it is straightforward, because many carers will not feel able to ask questions. Smaller groups with a constantly changing membership may have mixed agendas because people will have different needs. Groups with a constant membership are the ones which will be able to deal with personal information because people will learn to trust each other. A well-run group can be the best way of helping carers to say what they want to say and ask what they want to know. The reasons are obvious. It is when you know that your concerns are shared by the group, and that the group will support you, that you can speak up. Even the most sloppily run group can, of course, comfort carers; at the very least because they can feel that they are not alone.

Communication with colleagues

There are many types of colleagues: those of the same tribe or in the same team, those of another team or tribe and those above or below you. It can be helpful to see people from a different profession as from a different tribe. Like yours, their tribe has a different language, a different set of traditions and it spends a lot of time defending its position. Tribes tend to be competitive and defensive and often look down on other tribes in order to reinforce a sense of identity. It may be helpful to look at different levels in our own organisations in the same way.

So how do you set about communicating with another tribe? The first thing is to learn some of their language and traditions. It helps if they want to communicate with you so there is a meeting halfway. It is useful if you understand where they might compromise and where they might not. It helps to know what it is about your behaviour that makes them clam up and become defensive. There is a lot to be learnt from watching international disputes and the way these are worked out because it is the same thing on a different scale.

Personal relationships that overcome mutual suspicion are always helpful because then candid conversations can take place. It is striking how the original accord between Israel and the PLO was begun in informal, secret meetings on neutral territory in Norway. Presumably they began to see each other as people with reasons for behaving as they did. Mixed professional teams have the same result. People come to see each other as people with the same aims but different languages and priorities: no one is right or wrong and each brings a perspective that sheds some light on the situation. Many organisations are anxious about staff working in mixed professional teams because it dilutes their loyalty to the "tribe". Sometimes it is only those who feel themselves on the edge of the tribe anyway who really manage to work effectively in teams. Geriatricians, hospital social workers, health visitors and community police are examples of people often in this position.

What is needed is for us to bring the same thought we bring to the rest of our practice to this business of communicating with colleagues. Skills of diplomacy, negotiation, clarity, empathy are just as relevant. Written skills can be especially important when the opportunities of face-to-face communication are unavailable. GPs are a good illustration of this. They are seldom available for meetings and it is very important to communicate with them briefly and clearly in writing. The same can apply to colleagues in other parts of the organisation, who can become very defensive if they are wrong-footed by not having the necessary information. The emphasis in the community care procedures on written forms is an attempt to improve communication so that everyone is collecting the same information and the sharing mechanisms are clear.

Managers need to be especially careful about communication, since most of their problems can be laid at the door of incomplete or inadequate communication. Managers need to be able to share policies very clearly and to ensure that all those in their team can quote them back. Motivation is strongly linked to shared principles. In the field of dementia care, which is so fraught with ethical dilemmas, clear principles are vital. Communication needs to be verbal and in writing. Management by memo is never a good idea. Praise in public, rebuke in private is a good rule of thumb, as is being unstinting in praise. Caring for people with dementia is a very difficult and often thankless field of work: praise from a manager may be one source of job satisfaction.

Communication with the public
There is no doubt that there is much greater awareness of dementia now than there was even five years ago. The Alzheimer's Disease Society and Alzheimer Scotland - Action on Dementia have done remarkable work in raising awareness through their campaigns and through their awareness weeks. They are very skilful indeed at using the media. Of course there can be few people these days whose lives have not been touched by dementia, either within their family or in neighbours and friends.

Today, most people can talk about dementia, although they are often more comfortable using the term "Alzheimer's disease". Many older people are very frightened about the possibility that they might have dementia. After some upsetting experiences, I have learnt not to give false reassurance. People know only too well that something is wrong even if they seem to be functioning adequately. It is better to suggest that they talk to their GP who can do some tests or refer them for a full diagnosis. With the emergence of memory clinics more GPs will be able to refer these worried people once they have checked that their memory problems are not caused by illness, stress, depression or medication.

In Australia, a controversial journalist called Claudia Wright was diagnosed with early onset dementia and decided to share the experience on the media. As a result it became a lot more common to seek a neurological workover. One of the troubles in getting such a workover is that it can mean "a diagnosis and goodbye" at a time when people really need a lot of counselling. We seem inordinately slow at learning from the cancer world about this process of telling the diagnosis and following it up with support, information and counselling. The media, in many respects, are both raising awareness and responding to increasing public interest. Television has provided both highbrow and lowbrow programmes. Highbrow ones have looked at whether paintings by someone with dementia are "art" in the fascinating Late Show BBC programme on the American artist de Kooning, and the lowbrow have included soaps such as Eastenders, Casualty and The Bill. Fiction, too, is playing its part. Margaret Forster's moving book Have the Men Had Enough? (1989) painted a recognisable picture of the family stresses caused by dementia. More recently Michael Ignatieff's book Scar Tissue (1993), which is about inherited early-onset Alzheimer's disease, was shortlisted for the Booker Prize.

As staff in the field of dementia we too have a role in making sure that we share good information when we get the chance. The vast amount of readable and authoritative material produced by the Alzheimer's Disease Society and Alzheimer Scotland - Action on Dementia is freely available and in many languages. It is well worth having a good stock of it, not least to gently put right some of the misinformation so freely available. There are still far too many people who do not understand that it is a disease and not part of normal ageing. Memory does seem to deteriorate in old age to a degree, although this may be more about being unable to recall things rather than their not having been recorded in the first place. Dementia is a wholly different phenomenon and is a very great deal more frightening.

Chapter 4
Practical Help

Assessment

Assessment has received an extra degree of attention in the new world of assessment and care management. This chapter will focus on these general needs assessments rather than the more specific ones of particular professional groups, or for particular entitlements, such as those for attendance allowance. There are, of course, underlying principles for all assessments. It will also focus on the particular issues in assessing someone with dementia. Assessment of older people generally is covered very fully in Social Work with Older People (Marshall and Dixon 1995).

To many people, assessment now means using a form which both identifies need and records ability, or lack of it, to pay for services. The swing of the pendulum of policies on assessment is very evident at present between the professional model and the one prescribed by a form. The swing is well in the direction of the prescribed form and this must in part be a reaction to the failures of professional assessment. For too long professional assessment simply meant assessing eligibility for a service rather than what a person needed, independent of what was provided. Assessments were often too limited as well, sometimes because people felt some issues were not their responsibility and often because they did not know how to assess for a wider range of services. Social workers, for example, could usually ask the questions about money that the nurses found difficult, but they invariably left out the questions about health; both workers often left out the questions about housing. If all professionals are going to restrict themselves to assessing only the bits with which they are comfortable, then the answer is either a multiplicity of assessors or a form which gets all the information, albeit at a less-detailed level. In The White Paper Caring for People (1989) the Government quite specifically said they did not want to see a duplication of effort regarding assessment.

Much of the antagonism about forms is about their size, but, when consulted, professionals always opt for comprehensiveness rather than deciding what to omit. Forms are therefore likely to remain large and will, on the whole, require more than one visit. Some will require help from other professionals. An absurd attitude prevails in many places, that only social services/social work department staff can complete the forms. Given that a CPN, for example, may have worked with a family for months or years, he or she ought to be the person filling it in - jointly at the very least. I hope that by the time "I Can't Place This Place" is published this anomaly is sorted out.

Another reason for the comprehensive form is the obligation on social work/social services departments to assess need in their area in order to plan and purchase services. The idea is that full assessments of need will be aggregated to yield information on the needs of populations. (This will not, of course, include people who are not known to the services.) This means that forms embody information such that it can be counted rather than forms that simply have spaces for text. There are other advantages of having aggregated information needs, such as justifying the case for resources.

One of the problems related to needs assessment is how you translate difficulties into needs for services. Mrs Howard is incontinent and clearly needs help, but does she need a better sign on her toilet, a toilet downstairs, incontinence aids or treatment for a urinary tract infection? A form which lists difficulties does not tell you about needs. Mrs Howard might be depressed or demoralised and therefore not motivated to go to the toilet. There might be half a dozen ways of helping her with her depression which might ultimately improve her continence.

A form specifically for dementia based on a theoretical understanding of needs assessment: CarenapD, (McWalter et al, 1994) has been developed with intensive consultation and piloting in a research project in Fife. It has achieved a useful approach of listing a wide range of potential difficulties, asking for a tick as to whether these difficulties meant no need, met need or unmet need. The form then classifies types of help which might be required if the need is unmet. For example, Mrs Toner, who has dementia, has difficulty dressing herself and gets no help with this. The tick on the form would therefore identify that this need is unmet and highlight a range of options for meeting it including prompting, supervision or physical assistance, depending on her circumstances. The sophistication of this form is far beyond the usual forms of social work/social services departments. It is designed to meet the needs of any frontline worker and the managers and to be easily aggregated to provide information for planning. Managers of departments simply do not have the time or expertise on the whole to achieve this level of sophistication. It is intended that this form, training materials and the associated software will be available from the Dementia Services Development Centre at the University of Stirling.

In suggesting that the various professional staff working with people with dementia are not traditionally able to make a comprehensive assessment of need, it is not my intention to undermine the very real skills of assessment that have been developed. All the various staff working with people with dementia bring very special expertise. In my experience, medical and nursing staff are good at looking and smelling. They can read volumes into pallor and posture. Social workers are better at listening. They can hear between the lines when people describe their circumstances but they may fail to see something quite obvious like the thinness of the blankets. In general terms, most occupational therapists are good at looking too and often see the curled-up edge to the carpet and the inaccessible controls of the fire. Occupational therapists have solid expertise in assessing self-care skills, social workers are good at relationships and practical matters, and nurses at assessing important factors such as vitality and pain. I know there are countless exceptions to this set of stereotypes about professional expertise and limitations, but I have found it helpful to be aware that all staff have strengths and limitations, as a result of their training, often without being aware of them. In my view, if we do not recognise our special expertise, we will be less able to acknowledge that of others. We can learn a great many skills from each other through joint visiting and it is sad that these opportunities are so seldom taken.

Many experienced professionals feel very deskilled by forms which do not allow their worries and personal judgements to be recorded. The fact that they are expected to be read and agreed by the respondent further inhibits this use of professional experience and expertise. Of course, many so-called professional assessments were based on all manner of prejudice which is eliminated in current approaches but there are advantages and disadvantages in everything.

Another difficulty is weighing the relative value of an inevitably superficial comprehensive assessment with the richness of multiple assessments pulled together at team meetings. The latter can be very intrusive to people with dementia and their carers who get visited by numerous people all asking very personal, and often very similar, questions. Ideally, in complex cases we should have a joint visit by a couple of different professionals who can identify specific further assessments which are essential but who can collect most of the information required by all parties. In the UK, we have opted for one-person assessments using a form. In my view, we will soon begin to see that this is simply inadequate in complex cases where there must be some medical or nursing input. Australia's Aged Care Assessment Teams seem to be a model worth replicating. These are multidisciplinary teams who agree amongst themselves on the appropriate mix of people to do the first and any follow up assessments. This sometimes happens in dementia teams in the UK but it is very far from standard practice as it is in Australia.

Another kind of form which deserves to be more widely used is a dependency scale, such as the Modified Crichton Behaviour Rating Scale (MCBRS) (Corser et al 1991) and the Revised Elderly Persons Dependency Scale (REPDS) (McCulloch 1995). These are well-used instruments which give a rough-and-ready score on a range of types of dependency. I use the description "rough-and-ready" deliberately because researchers are often dismayed by the belief of staff in the absolute accuracy of a score or numerical measure. The scales also tend to focus on the negative, but on the other hand they provide a usefully broad picture. The REPDS, for example, assesses dependency across seven areas:

- physical
- confusion
- behaviour.
- nursing
- sociability
- psychiatric
- self-care

However rough-and-ready the scores, they are a great improvement on meaning-less descriptions such as "moderate dementia" and they do provide a shared language. They are also useful for assessing changes over time. Another dimension that is not receiving the attention it deserves is the biographical approach to assessment (Dant et al 1989), which is based on the view that people cope with illness in old age in the way they have coped with other difficulties in the past and need the same kind of help which worked in the past. Assessments using this approach therefore look at the history of the people being assessed. This has the additional advantage of leading to a much closer relationship between the assessor and the assessed, because so much has been shared and people being assessed feel that they are known as people. However, the current, rather mechanistic, approach to assessment and care planning does not really accommodate such involvement. Assessment procedures may change as we learn that motivation and relationships are the key to coping as much as any amount of tailored care packages.

One of the problems with forms is that they tend to measure only what is measur-able. Thus they can ask whether or not you can go upstairs and whether or not you can bath yourself. Others focus on likely causes of stress, such as incontinence or behaviour problems. However, research suggests (for example, Nolan et al 1990) that it is the carer's subjective perception of events and circumstances that is more important in determining stress, and, to some extent, the outcome, than the events themselves. This is very difficult to incorporate in a form. Forms are also less good at the key issues of relationships and motivation. This has been found to be crucial in recent research (Levin et al 1994). Other research (Levin and Meredith

1988) has underlined the importance of the relationship before the onset of the disease in people's capacity to continue caring. People who said they intended to go on, come what may, usually lasted longer than those who were less certain. This sounds obvious, but a lot of research has been on factors which are more measurable, such as the combination of services that enable people to carry on rather than the motivation of the key participants.

Another problem is turning difficulties into needs. Miss Harris, whom we met in Chapter 1, became more paranoid as her dementia progressed. She was unable to explain to herself why she constantly lost her keys, her purse and her groceries and blamed the woman upstairs. She began to believe that the woman upstairs had magical powers to penetrate her walls and sneak in to steal her belongings. She lived alone, had no close family and her niece lived five hundred miles away. She said that she could manage on her pension, but was unable to go out of the house to do her shopping in case the neighbour slipped in and robbed her.

What did Miss Harris need? She claimed she needed nothing except the removal of the neighbour upstairs. Another neighbour who was constantly being disturbed by Miss Harris to find her keys or her purse said that she thought Miss Harris needed to be assessed to see if her paranoia could be treated. This neighbour also wanted Miss Harris talked into a frame of mind where she would accept help with her shopping and meals.

This divergence of views also illustrates the point made already in this book: the conflict of interests. Miss Harris's neighbour could have done a great deal more for her in terms of reducing her anxiety by helping her find things and reassuring her constantly that they were not stolen, merely mislaid, but this neighbour had other commitments including a demanding job. She was unwilling to relinquish much of her social life to looking after Miss Harris, although Miss Harris always told professionals who visited how attentive the neighbour was and how she could call on her for help at any time of the day or night.

One problem specific to dementia is the capacity people with it possess to perform for a short period. They seem to be able to rally all their resources to appear quite normal for the duration of a meeting which they understand to be important.

This is intensely exasperating for the carer who then has to convince the person doing the assessment that the person with dementia was not usually so competent. This is very awkward for carers who can feel very disloyal. A longer visit is often a way round this since few people with dementia can sustain such an effort for more than an hour.

Finally, people with dementia have constantly changing needs. Many couples manage to cope sharing a fine blend of skills: sometimes the physically disabled but mentally alert person is the brains and the other with dementia the arms and legs. Then one falls ill and overnight a previous assessment is redundant. A few weeks later the status quo is restored but perhaps there is a loss of nerve in either or both. People with dementia function a lot less well when they are anxious, and sometimes a disturbance to a familiar regime may cause such anxiety that they never fully recover past competence. Because assessment is such a huge topic, I have focused in this section on general assessments in the community, which are the responsibility of the local authority, rather than looking at those different undertaken by other staff. I have tried to make the point that the best assessments pull in the expertise of many staff. Many of the points raised apply to any assessment. They also apply to reassessments and reviews which are always essential, especially in this field where needs can change as the disease progresses. Assessment is as vital as diagnosis and one needs both.

Diagnosis
The importance of a good diagnosis is a recurring theme of this book. For non-medical staff, the issue is how to ensure that this is done. A GP skilled in dementia will be well able to make a diagnosis in a straightforward case. She or he should take a good history from the patient and other informants, in order to obtain evidence of global impairment and to rule out other diagnoses. A blood test should also be done. Both people in the early stages, when diagnosis is very tricky, and difficult cases should be referred to a specialist. One of the problems is the uninterested GP who does not have the skills to make the diagnosis and should be encouraged to make a referral. This can be a very delicate business but one at which community and practice nurses are real experts. Sometimes the consultant can assist and advise about how to get the GP to make a referral. Very few consultant psychiatrists run an open referral system like the one Professor Murphy runs from Guy's Hospital in London. She has weathered the objections of GPs who are now ardent supporters. It seems unlikely that the Government is going to risk the initial wrath of GPs by encouraging more open access to diagnostic services.

Getting an early diagnosis is a key issue for positive and negative reasons. The positive ones are that patients and their families can make plans, obtain information and receive what help there is available. A wrong diagnosis is a disaster because of the implications for the patient and the family and it is this which makes GPs understandably anxious and leads them to prevaricate. Changes to Fund Holding GPs and Trust Status will complicate the relationship between GPs and consultants, and may well make follow-up more difficult in that GPs may be less willing to pay for assistance from a Trust-employed consultant psychiatrist.

Telling and sharing

The current emphasis on hearing the voice of consumers of services has implications for both assessment and diagnosis. Certainly the best way to get around the interrogatory nature of form filling is to do it alongside the respondent so that they choose what is written in the boxes and on the lines. Sitting side by side and going through it together diminish a lot of the paranoia because in a sense the information is then jointly owned. Most forms now require that the respondent signs and this is a great deal more appropriate if they have helped to fill it in. There are difficulties when a joint form is done for both the carer and the person with dementia, especially if they do not agree, which is very likely. Some authorities dispense two forms and try to have them filled in separately.

This approach does, of course, assume that the person with dementia and the assessor can achieve some degree of agreement. There is a complex issue here about whether forms are meant to be a reflection of the professional assessment or the user assessment. This has tended to be glossed over. Miss Harris would probably have said that she had no needs except the removal of her upstairs neighbour, although it might just have been possible to get her to admit her distress at her failing memory. Many people with dementia refuse services and much of this is related to fear. They know that their ability to cope is on a knife-edge and they often have elaborate systems for remembering. Often these are about having everything they need in sight, so there are piles of food and clothes in every available space. If these were tidied away they would be lost. They are also, probably rightly, afraid that if an outsider knew how poorly they coped they would not be allowed to continue as they are. Miss Harris had everything she needed for meals lined up on her sofa where she could see it. This looked chaotic to outsiders, especially since it included empty packets to remind her that they were finished.

The whole process of assessment can be therapeutic if the person doing it has the necessary skills. It can provide the opportunity to review what is going on, and for the carer and the cared-for to address their needs together or separately. Some carers do not even see themselves as carers with needs and the whole process leads them to stop and confront their situation. Some have not liked to face the fact that the person they are caring for might be ill rather than simply old; for them the possibility that their relative may have a very trying terminal illness may be too much to bear. Similarly, persons with dementia may not have stopped to address their needs or those of their relative. They are likely to know that something is wrong with their brain, but often they have not faced up to it, far less talked about it.

Mrs Kane had wholly unrealistic expectations of what her daughter would do for her both now and when her dementia had progressed. Her CPN had to get mother and daughter together for a discussion in which the daughter was encouraged to set limits. The planning of help was then on a much more open and practical level which stood them in good stead as time passed.

Working with people with dementia and their carers is highly skilled and potentially very harassing work although it has huge rewards. Assessment is one of those intervention points with huge potential for both a positive and a negative experience. Workers who wander into assessment without having thought through what might happen are unwise and may find themselves unable to take advantage of the therapeutic opportunities. At the very least workers should think through beforehand what they would do if the person with dementia asks about diagnosis; the relative says they are not coping; they both get into an argument about how much trouble the person with dementia is causing, and so on. Joint visits with an experienced worker are an excellent way to learn.

Sharing the diagnosis is increasingly seen as good practice and has already been mentioned in the communication section. Usually this is seen as the responsibility of the person who made it - either the hospital specialist or the GP. There are many variations in practice and we have yet to learn enough from the world of cancer. Some doctors prefer to tell the whole family, with the person with dementia present. They claim that this sets a standard of treating the person with dementia as an adult, which then makes relationships more straightforward as the disease progresses. Others tell the carer and the person with dementia but tell them separately. Some simply tell the carer. Sometimes the decision is made on the basis of a judgement about what the person with dementia wants and this is obviously the right thing to do. Occasionally it is based on the preference of the doctor, which is clearly not right. There is a need for a great deal more written material and training on this issue of telling. Staff support is vital too.

Non-medical staff, as in the field of cancer, often find themselves sharing the diagnosis either because the person did not hear the doctor or because they did not feel comfortable asking for the diagnosis to be repeated and explained. Providing the right amount of information is not easy. Some people will want euphemisms such as "memory problems", others will want all the details. Leaving written information can be useful so the person with dementia and the carer can read as much or as little as they can deal with.

Care management

Care management is one of those ideas which is plainly sensible and a reaction against years of inflexible provision of standard services. As such, it has been welcomed without perhaps a real understanding of the negative as well as the undoubted positive outcomes. It is also easy to muddle up outcomes which are the result of related policies, rather than of care management itself. In the UK we have assumed that care management means a multiplicity of providers, since we have assumed that it is impossible to provide a flexible, individually tailored package of services from the local authority. In Geelong in Australia, however, the community options programme (a care management programme for dementia sufferers and their carers) was using mainly council services, but had managed to make them a great deal more flexible by threatening to buy more flexible services elsewhere. Negative outcomes include the fact that providers can be smaller agencies with few opportunities for training and poor conditions of service for staff, or even individuals with no protection against exploitation at all. The emphasis on cost and charging was not, I think, fully understood prior to the implementation of the NHS and the Community Care Act in April 1993. It has become a difficult and contentious issue for people with dementia as mentioned in Chapter 2 (Langan and Means 1995).

Perhaps more positively there is an incredible change in the availability of flexible services - ones that cover the evening, the weekends and overnight, if you are lucky enough to live where services are well developed. A real geographical lottery is emerging.

Mrs Williamson illustrates how people can remain in the community with a lot of services, although rarely without the help of neighbours and family. Mrs Williamson was an eighty-four-year-old diabetic woman with dementia. Some days she was very much in touch, but most of the time she was very confused, often failing to use the toilet so her flat could be very unpleasant. She lived alone on the third floor of a small block of flats in an overspill estate with neighbours who had moved in with her some twenty-five years ago. None of her four children remained local although one son visited most weekends. Her care plan consisted of four days of day care (in two different day centres, since no local day centre in her area operates for more than two days per week), a daily home help on weekdays, a tuck-in service every day, mobile domiciliary help at weekends and regular visits from her district nurse for the diabetes. In spite of this range of help, the neighbours were called upon at all times of the day and night. Luckily one was a nurse, but she sometimes resented the intrusion in spite of being very fond of Mrs Williamson.

Increasingly, if you are able to pay, there is an astonishing range of services to help you. There is a possibility that those who are well off will benefit enormously, as will those who are on income support and in very great need. Those who have less urgent need and those who are above the poverty level, but not rich, will suffer. Many are likely to refuse help if they have to pay for it; this should have been evident in the planning stages when "targeting" kept being mentioned, but not really talked about. Instead it has come as something of a shock to many frontline workers who see people in extreme need refusing services. Mr Potter was seventy-five and cared for his wife who had dementia and his forty-year-old son who had Down's syndrome. He had been much helped over the years by home helps, who did the shopping and helped him keep the house clean. When charges were introduced for the home help service he thought he could manage without them. Three weeks later he died from a heart attack whilst carrying heavy bags from the supermarket.

One problem with our system is that care management is not an interdisciplinary business as it is in Australia. This means that we have limited opportunity to provide a seamless health and social work service. Dementia makes special challenges for individual care managers. Care plans have to be constantly reviewed and updated. Staff also have to be up to date themselves in the constant shifting of services available and the criteria of eligibility. Then there are the abrupt changes, for example sudden deterioration with multi-infarct dementia, which can throw the best care plan into disarray. There is also the issue of control. Who is in charge of a care plan? Some carers feel very diminished with someone else managing the help they receive. As I said in the communication section, one essential skill with carers is to be able to give help in a way that makes them feel in control. Control is also an issue of conflict of interests. Who decides that Mr Slater needs to go for day care if he wants to stay at home and his wife desperately needs a break? What if people refuse help, like Miss Harris, yet the care manager knows that they will only survive if there is some help going in? Staff may need skills in selling services. Would Mr Slater accept the idea of going to a club and Miss Harris the concept of a "companion"?

Dementia is a challenging field to work in because it raises a host of ethical issues as well as practical ones. How much self-determination is reasonable? There is no easy answer to this. Like all ethical issues the answer is a balance: in this case between self-determination and the right to care and protection. Ethical questions need to be constantly asked by teams of staff as well as by individuals. Miss Harris, for example, wanted to be left alone. There was clearly a danger of malnutrition and poor self-care. If she was allowed to choose and then found dead, the visiting staff might have been in some difficulty from their managers if they had had a different view of the balance between self-determination and the duty of care.

Claiming welfare benefits
Being old in Britain means you have a good chance of being on a low income. Many people on pensions are on incomes just above the income support levels because of small occupational pensions or savings. Very few people on pensions have incomes anywhere near the average wage. This means that constant vigilance is required by workers to ensure that basic benefits are claimed as soon as people become eligible.

There are also benefits which are available because there is someone who needs care in the household. For people who need constant care during the day or round the clock there are the Attendance Allowances. The most important are Disability Living Allowance for those aged under sixty-six and Attendance Allowance for those aged over sixty-five. It is very important that these are claimed by all those entitled to them. People need to spell out on the forms, in precise detail, the help that is required. For example, rather than saying that Mrs Murdoch needs help in toileting, it is better to say that Mrs Murdoch needs help going to the toilet about twelve times during the day and four times at night. The more detail given, the more chance of success. People also need to be encouraged to appeal if they are turned down because eligibility hangs on arbitrary interpretation of words like "require frequent attention" or "for a significant part of the day". For this reason, having someone to help with an appeal makes a real difference. Welfare rights staff will know how to interpret these terms for an appeal.

Disability Living Allowance has two components: mobility and care. It is the latter which is applicable to people with dementia since it is paid at three rates. The lower rate is appropriate for many people in the early stages of dementia and the highest for people in the moderate to severe stages. The Attendance Allowance is basically the same although it does not have the lowest rate.

Application forms now come in a pack. The first form is completed by or on behalf of the person requiring care. The second is completed by the doctor or someone similar; it may be worth considering if the GP is the best person if he or she does not know the person with dementia well. A district nurse or health visitor who has been involved, and who can put down all the initials after their name, may be a much better person. There are always delays on attendance allowance and you may need to warn the carers about this. The carer may also need to be warned that local authorities often charge for services if someone is on attendance allowance.

You may find you have to advise people to claim basic income support. Pensioners are major under-claimers even of this very basic benefit. They will get the pensioner premium(s) automatically, but they might even be eligible for the severe disability premium which is payable to people on attendance allowance. They also may be eligible for community care grants from the social fund. The receipt of all these benefits can mean a major increase in income for someone with a lot of care costs. Finally, certain people are exempt from the property part of the Council Tax because they are severely mentally impaired and in receipt of a benefit such as Attendance Allowance. GPs vary in their willingness to sign the forms and some are working on very out-of-date records, so help may be needed to sort this out. Some will charge for doing the paperwork. Carers themselves, if they might otherwise be working, can claim Invalid Care Allowance but they should take advice before claiming it. They and the person they are caring for may lose benefits related to income support. The arithmetic is complicated because Invalid Care Allowance gives carers access to the care premium of income support and Class 1 contribution credits for National Insurance and access to sickness benefit.

Age Concern produces a very straightforward and useful guide to welfare benefits called Your Rights. It is one thing to know what benefits are available; it is quite another to persuade people to claim them. Many people with dementia have very great difficulty understanding the constantly changing benefits system and may require the help of an Appointee (see legal section). Carers may find the whole business too humiliating. You often find someone who is unwilling to claim because they have claimed before and been turned down. This makes people feel as if they have been trying to fiddle the system and they require a lot of support to try again. Another problem is that Attendance Allowance is often only granted on appeal, but it is very difficult to get people to appeal.

Many local authorities are being much more energetic in their welfare rights work in order to then charge recipients of Attendance Allowance for services they receive. In spite of the charges it is invariably worth encouraging people to claim.

The principles and the rules of eligibility are formidably complex and deter many people from making a claim. One of the most useful ways of motivating them to try is to get the support of a body such as a carers' group. Discussion of benefits and the realisation that other people have gone through the hoops, sometimes successfully, can give carers confidence because it diminishes the stigma. Workers in the field can cajole at length but it really needs to be someone in a similar position to show the way.

Advocacy
It has proved remarkably difficult to establish advocacy schemes in the field of dementia care. They have traditionally been best established in the field of learning disability. There ought to be all sorts of transfers of expertise and experience between the two fields, since many of the issues are the same. It must be, in part, to do with a general public fear of people with dementia and a failure to realise that a lot of people with it can respond to a stranger who is genuinely interested. Very difficult situations where an advocate would be useful can often arise. One is the visiting daughter syndrome illustrated here by Mrs McNeice. Mrs McNeice's daughter lived in the USA. On one of her visits she decided that her mother could no longer cope at home and got her admitted to a nursing home in spite of remonstrations from the social worker and daughter-in-law. She arranged for the house to be sold to pay the fees. Mrs McNeice was acutely distressed by the move and the speed of change. She died some weeks later. Both the social worker and the daughter-in-law felt very guilty that they had not done more to prevent the move and they would have welcomed an agency with a clear task of representing the interests of the person with dementia. In Victoria, a referral to the Office of the Public Advocate would have been possible but we have, as yet, nothing of this type in the UK.

Where advocacy schemes are taking on people with dementia, there is certainly a need for careful training and support of advocates, whether they are to be involved over a length of time or for a particular episode, such as the closure of a ward. They need to know how important it is to obtain as much information as possible about the background of the person, perhaps using the life-story book approach. This is in part to aid communication but also to help work out what it is the person with dementia would have wanted to say had they been able to say it. They need to know a lot about communication as mentioned already in Chapter 2. They need to know that many people with dementia have fluctuating competence in communication and that they need to persevere or wait until a better time. They need to be able to manage non-verbal communication. Anyone, for example, who cannot bear to touch someone else is unlikely to be suitable for this work because so much communication is through touch.

It is puzzling that there are so few advocacy schemes given the dire need for advocacy for people with dementia who tend to be treated as of very low status. Many of them have outlived their relatives, if they ever had them, and have nobody to represent their interests. Advocates, who are basically people with no vested interest, are sorely needed to represent the views of people with dementia in the countless decisions that are made about and for them. In longstay wards, for example, advocates could help in the making of good, considered decisions about locked doors and other restraints, about activity programmes, about outings, and so on. In any longstay establishment, there are many occasions where decisions are made which would benefit from someone giving a stronger voice to the person with dementia. Most provider agencies such as NHS Trusts and private residential and nursing homes will have policies on user involvement in decisions. These policies will often mention advocacy.

Reviews in residential care homes are a frequent source of concern to staff. They can be very harassing to the person with dementia who sits in what feels like a room full of strangers. Mrs Ogilvie, for example, had settled well into a home until the review. She understood that discussions were taking place about whether or not she should stay. The meeting left her very anxious and insecure not least because of the people she did not know who were talking about her. She did not understand that the decision was made that she should stay, and her behaviour became very restless and agitated. An advocate might have insisted that fewer people were present and might have spoken clearly and firmly on her behalf.

Advocacy should not be seen as combative, as taking on the world on behalf of a person who cannot speak for themselves. Rather it should be seen as giving people with dementia a voice in a world where they are generally silent. By asking questions and seeking clarification the advocate can assist everyone to pause and think again about decisions from the point of view of the person with dementia. This should make for better decisions and more peace of mind all round, since justice is seen to be done.

Food

Food plays a big part in any work with people with dementia and their carers. In fact, it plays a big part in all our lives but we are so accustomed to it that we give it little thought most of the time. There are many dimensions and this section can only raise some issues in order to get food onto the agenda of all staff in this field.

How do we ensure that people with dementia are getting good nourishment? This is very important since we need to be sure that nothing is interfering with their ability to function at the highest possible level. Lack of food or poor quality food can mean that people are listless, constipated and constantly poorly, all of which militate against good intellectual functioning. Even if you have not experienced lack of good nutrition you will probably know, for instance, how your general performance diminishes, if you are constipated.

There are different issues in different settings. At home it may be that a person with dementia is not remembering to eat or to eat properly. Sometimes people do not recognise meals on wheels containers as food. If they are living with a relative, the relative may be too weary to prepare nourishing meals. There is, of course, always the issue of money. Can the person with dementia or the relative afford to buy good food? Day care is one way of ensuring a decent meal. It may be worth inviting the relative to lunch as well if you are also anxious about their food intake. People visiting the homes of people with dementia need to be aware that, because people with dementia often need to see things if they are not to forget them, the food may be literally lying around. Sometimes they will see a lot of uneaten food, such as meals on wheels cartons, stacked up in the kitchen.

In residential and nursing homes, the nutrition ought to be satisfactory because the registration teams will have considered the menus. In all settings there is the problem of people with dementia not wanting to eat, or not wanting a balanced diet. There seems to be a tendency for people with dementia to want food that is easier to eat: mashed or minced food or food with a lot of gravy. They usually want more sweet food. It can be exasperating to watch them push away perfectly good food in preference for ice-cream or jelly. Really nourishing soups and good quality ice-cream may meet a wide range of nutritional requirements but supplements in the form of pills or drinks are worth considering if you are doubtful about someone's diet.

There may be other reasons why people are not eating. It may be that their mouth is sore and they cannot explain this to you except by spitting out food. It may be that they are using food as a means of communication about their despair, anger and frustration, which we mentioned in the section on communication. It may be that they find the whole business of meal times too stressful. If you think this last might be the case try finger food. Enticing, moist and easy to eat sandwiches, nourishing kinds of cakes such as banana and carrot, traybakes and nibbles provided frequently throughout the day can help people to eat plenty. It is thought that there may be an issue of blood sugar in the behaviour of some people with dementia. Many of them need a steady supply of food, not large quantities but often and highly calorific to remain calm.

Some people with dementia clearly have eating disorders not unlike anorexia. They can refuse food. This may again be a form of communication, perhaps saying "I want to die", or it may be a more complex psychiatric condition. The same applies to uncontrolled overeating which, although rare, can lead to obesity. It seems as though some people may have no recollection of the fact that they have just eaten and eat anything they can. This again may be a symptom of a more complex psychiatric malaise.

Not all failure to eat is about the food itself. Sometimes food is put down in front of the person and then removed twenty minutes later without any effort at encouragement or any record being taken of the lack of intake. At times actually feeding people is carried out in such a humiliating way that the person with dementia derives no pleasure from the food and may refuse it. Occasionally meal times are chaos and staff fail to see that someone with dementia has forgotten how to use the implements. It is always desirable for staff to sit and eat with people with dementia to ensure that meal times are calm and enjoyable.

This leads on to the potential for food and meal times as an activity. There is vast potential. There is the planning, the shopping, the preparation, the cooking, the table laying, the eating, the clearing, the tidying up, the washing up and the putting away. There are activities for almost everyone in this: something familiar which they can do well and be appreciated for. There is also potential for one-off activities such as celebrating festivals or entertaining. These are natural activities which are intensely familiar and enjoyable so they will be discussed further in the activities section of the next chapter.

Design
Most people working directly with dementia sufferers will have given little thought to the buildings they work in unless the premises are particularly unsuitable. However, it is worth reflecting on the extent to which buildings disable people with dementia because they simply cannot make sense of them. This results in them feeling that they are in the wrong place. Many people with dementia, for example, imagine they are in a place of work such as a factory rather

than their residence. They vary greatly in their ability to find their way around buildings but, in principle, we should try to make buildings as easy as possible so that as many people as possible can find their own way to where they want to go. This is especially important in relation to the toilet since not being able to find it can cause great anxiety, high and sometimes unnecessary dependence on staff and frequent incontinence.

A general consensus in relation to some tried and tested principles is emerging from the research and expertise of people in design from many countries, for example Cohen and Day (1993). There is a need to keep units small so that people with dementia have as little to learn as possible. Domestic style is another sensible approach, since most people will be better able to make sense of a place that is familiar in this sense. Most people have lived in a domestic setting for the greater part of their lives. Local facilities will have the additional advantages of a familiar environment and ease of access for staff and visitors as well as providing easy access to normal activities in a familiar neighbourhood for the people with dementia.

Then there is the need to avoid corridors because they are very disorientating and invariably direct people straight through the fire door! "See and be seen" is a good design principle since people with dementia can be very anxious if they cannot see a member of staff. Carers will tell you that the person with dementia usually likes to have the carer in sight which can be very irksome in an ordinary house. In longstay and daycare settings this means ideally that units are open plan with only waist-high partitions and bedrooms opening into living rooms. Being able to see a toilet from anywhere in the unit is very important.

Good lighting is needed for people with dementia to function at their best, as is space. Light so that they can see where they are going, and space because people with dementia often walk in a rather indirect way and tend to bang into things if there is not enough space. Space to walk is often important, although less so if there is an understandable design and plenty of distractions. Walking space should seem to go somewhere, perhaps around the furniture and out into the garden and then along a path and back through another door. Outside space which is safe but does not feel like a prison yard is invaluable. The best gardens have planting against the fence and possess distractions. Ferrard House (Gibson 1991) has an old-fashioned turf cart and a small fountain through millstones as well as a lot of benches. Shadows and reflections should be avoided. Shadows can be seen as solid obstacles, reflections as pools of water. Colour is less effective than objects as a way of identifying doors and key areas. People lose the ability to differentiate colour except perhaps in the red/yellow range, but they are more likely to recognise a plant, a door knocker or a wall hanging. Contrasts in floor covering may be seen as steps. Pictures of fruit and vegetables on wallpaper may be seen as the real thing.

Finally, the principle of different rooms for different functions is important. People with dementia need to be able to see what a room is for in order to adjust themselves to what is required. Dining-rooms should look like dining-rooms, and sitting-rooms like sitting-rooms. Single bedrooms can afford a wonderful opportunity to provide a place that assists in orientating people with dementia to their own identity. In my view they should be let unfurnished to ensure that familiar personal furniture and possessions are brought in, but this is rarely possible. Built-in furniture can and should be avoided. The odd photograph or ornament is not enough.

Given this list of tips, what can be done with a building which already exists as a day centre or longstay facility? Imagination is needed, and many staff are very good at seeing the world through the eyes of someone who has no recent memory and impaired ability to work things out. They can see how a corridor can be made easier to understand. The staff at Walker House (Bell 1992), for example, decided that their corridor would make more sense as a landing of a Scottish tenement and they have made all the bedroom doors look like front doors, put in gaslights and metal signs and have put traditional Scottish brass name-plates on the doors. This has apparently made very good sense to the residents, most of whom will have lived in tenements in Glasgow.

Staff often ask about signs. The answer is, try and see. They work really well with some people if they are at the right height and if they relate to something the person with dementia understands. There is no point, for example, in those modern plastic stick figures we have on toilet doors. There may be a point in the words "Ladies" or "Gents", or perhaps a picture of the toilet itself. Some staff are affronted at the thought of signs, especially explicit ones, on doors. In my view, anything which helps people with dementia retain the dignity of independence is worthwhile, but it is likely that different signs will be needed by different people.

Bedroom signs are a real challenge because different things will work with different people. Some will remember their name, others a number, others will need a picture or an object. Photographs may make sense but may not. I am always excited when I listen to staff who have really tried to find something that works for particular individuals. In one home I found staff had been baffled by three women for whom photographs, drawings, objects or door-knockers did not work. They hit upon using the numbers of their former residences, which worked fine. In Norway I visited a home which actually installed people's own front doors when this was possible, whilst in Shetland I saw a home where some people still recognised the name of their house so this was used.

Technology

Readers may find it odd to have a relatively substantial section on technology in a book on dementia. Given that alarm systems are the extent of technology familiar to most of us, and the fact that they are, on the whole, useless with people with dementia it may seem particularly surprising. However, technology is the shape of things to come and all of us in this field have got to be on the alert to ensure that it is used with the best interests of people with dementia at heart. In this section I propose to look at the range of technologies that is available and then raise some issues about its use.

I think there are perhaps as many as ten kinds of technology to consider in terms of what they do. Many of them overlap one or more of the following functions but I find the distinction helpful.

- remind
- stimulate
- relax
- compensate
- manage behaviour

- safety
- surveillance
- control
- communication
- co-ordinate services

Reminder devices are appearing which can warn people which windows they have left open when they leave the house, or which appliances are still on. Sometimes it is a simple light at the front door which lights up, sometimes a box which tells you what is wrong. If accommodation is wired up to a computer, it can be programmed to suit the needs of the individual. I might, for example, constantly forget my iron and you might leave your windows open. The equipment can be programmed to suit us. Another reminder device is a board connected to the telephone with photographs which are pressed to get a number. It can help someone who has forgotten telephone numbers and is no longer able to look them up.

There are computer programmes appearing which stimulate, or claim to stimulate, people with dementia. They might have reminiscence material on them or puzzles which are adult but are also achievable. They seem to be using a touch screen rather than a keyboard. Mrs Mancroft, who has dementia, claims that she needs to do computer games as soon as she gets out of bed in the morning to kick her brain into action.

Numerous technologies are appearing to relax people with dementia. Snoezelen rooms (Benson 1994) are equipped with soft textures, gently moving light, relaxing sound, warmth and pleasant smells. I have also seen them with a reclining chair which gently pummels the back as you lie in it. I noticed that its main use was for stressed staff!

Compensatory devices are those which compensate for deficits, such as the technology which turns off a bath when it is almost overflowing or turns off the stove when a saucepan is empty.

Few technologies have yet been used to manage behaviour in a positive way but it seems to me to be only a matter of time. There are plenty of people who become very restless at dusk as the light diminishes. Others can become very bad tempered when they are too hot. It seems to me to be relatively simple to have a device which sustains a light level or a temperature level.

Safety devices are more familiar in the world of dementia care. They are the devices which allow a carer to turn off the gas cooker and to turn it on again when they are present. Similar devices exist which lock the controls of a fire off but can be unlocked if there is someone else there to supervise.

Similarly, surveillance devices are not new. Here I mean things like video cameras and tagging. The latter takes many forms. There are wrist devices which ring whenever a person goes through a radio ring or a particular door. Devices which ring bells when someone goes through a door probably come under this heading too. Although they are less person specific, they are often installed to deal with a particular person. Passive alarms are certainly a kind of surveillance. These include gadgets under bed mats or mats at the bathroom door. They record somewhere else when trodden on. New devices can also record when someone gets out of bed. They can be under the foot of the bed or a passive infra-red system like a burglar alarm. Almost all of these can be programmed round a particular individual. They might, for example, only be switched on between the hours of midnight and 5am for someone who gets out of bed and forgets to go back again.

Control technology seems to me to be that which actually prevents someone doing something they want to do such as exotic door locks which are operable only by people with a memory for numbers.

Relatives have long depended on the telephone - a very familiar kind of technology - for social contact. The emergence of video phones and computer communication systems opens up a host of possibilities for carers. It might be communication in terms of access to information, of contact with a service provider or have social intercourse applicabilities. Alarm systems, whilst not useful for people with dementia, might be so for carers if they need help in an emergency. They are certainly useful if staff need to call for help.

Communication for people with dementia is less likely to be assisted by technology unless they are already familiar with it. It might be, for example, that a person with a lifetime of keyboard skills may still be able to type a message. There are two books written by people with dementia (Davis 1993 and Friel McGowin 1993) and both authors claim they were able to use a computer after they were no longer able to write.

Finally, computer co-ordination for service providers becomes more sophisticated all the time. With wider use of portable computers it is possible to plug in your records and have them copied onto other people's systems. Similarly a PC in a person's residence can be used for all visiting staff to update their records and can be linked to central records as well.

It is tempting, but I think unhelpful, to see some sorts of technology as positive and others as negative. It seems to me that it is the way it is used which is either positive or negative. It would be only too easy to use the relaxing technologies to stupefy someone, for example. Conversely, tagging devices can give an energetic person a chance to move about more freely.

Many issues arise in the use of technology, many of them similar to the use of any input such as drugs or restraint. There always has to be a question of who it is benefiting. Clearly one would hope that it was always the person with dementia but this cannot be assumed. It might well be the carer. It might be the provider of the service, who feels able to provide fewer staff if technology is in place. This may not of course be a bad thing. Some visits are very intrusive and technology might afford more privacy. A small group home was going to reduce its night staff on the grounds that videos and passive alarm systems were in place. The staff vociferously pointed out that video cameras cannot wipe away tears, or change a wet sheet, or hold a hand.

Another tricky issue is that of consent. Consent must be voluntary, competent and informed. This is very difficult with a lot of technologies. In this field, as I have said before, we are used to constantly balancing the need to treat the person with dementia as an adult with rights and responsibilities and the duty we have to ensure they are properly cared for. It is not an easy balancing act but one that is very important with technology.

In my view, any technology which removes the liberties of someone with dementia should be treated as one would a restraint. Its use should be recorded under the same headings listed previously in the restraint section:

- What is the problem and why is it a problem?

- What other methods have been tried to deal with this problem?

- Details of the full discussion with relatives and other key people in the person's life (advocacy may need to be considered for people without relatives and friends)

- What decision was made about the technology to be used and by whom?

- Firm time limits specified.

- Specified time for review and who will be involved.

Chapter 5
Making It Work

Service development
Service development is an area of work which some people do without thinking and other people never think of doing. It ought to be firmly part of the repertoire of skills of everyone in this field because there is such a severe shortfall of services. The ideal approach is when a member of staff identifies a gap in services based on good analysis of good information, gets the right group of people together who produce a plan which is then set in motion. This is very rare. More often, a group of staff, such as a local team, collect information but omit the careful analysis and rush straight onto a project. This is usually a project they have read about in Community Care or Nursing Mirror. It may or may not be relevant. Another way things happen is that a group of activists identify resources and set up a service. A frequent example of this is the church group with an underused church hall. The problem with this approach is that the services are often in the wrong place because areas with extra, unused resources are not always those of greatest need. The most usual approach is when money suddenly becomes available and there is a mad planning phase and the project, which meets the criteria and seems possible, is submitted.

This sounds very critical whereas it is, in my experience, how the world works. It is very hard to collect information, analyse it carefully, work out what is required and where it should be, and then to wait for the opportunity and the money. It is equally hard to motivate a group of activists if there is little chance of success. People are usually so busy that they only make space for meetings and working parties when they can see a pay off. Planning is in a sense everybody's job and nobody's job. It should happen at various different levels with joint planning doing the broad brush identification of gaps, and joint groups at a lower level setting about the local planning and implementation phase. The various levels of planning and the different planning remits can be confusing, but knowing how it all works makes it possible to feed the right concerns, information and ideas into the process. For staff at the coal-face, team discussions about individuals can indicate where there are shared problems for which planning is required. The trouble with dementia is that there is often so little interest and so little awareness of both need and possibilities that very little happens unless real enthusiasts set about making it happen, with or without enough information collection and the right people on board.

So what are the skills, assuming that you are a frontline worker or a first-level manager? First is information collection. What is the population of your area? Are there lots of young old people or old old people? It is more likely to be the latter since this would reflect the population as a whole but places like new towns have young old populations. Ideally you need to obtain an age breakdown in five-year sections: 60-64, 65-69, 70-74 etc. Jorm and Korten (1988) have found that the prevalence of dementia doubles every five years. They analysed a lot of prevalence studies and found they came up with very different numbers. What they had in common was the exponential curve. If you assume a starting point of 0.7 per cent people with dementia in the age group 60-64 you can take it from there. You can thus produce a rough and ready estimate of the numbers of people with dementia using this formula. You might then want to know a few things about your population such as the numbers on income support and the numbers of older people living on their own. Figures such as the basic population and their characteristics are almost always available from headquarters. It may be the planning department of the health authority or the social services/social work department; it may be the housing department; it may be your own department.

You then need to find out what services there are. "Mapping" all these data - ideally on clear plastic sheets, so you can lay one on top of the other to at once see the full picture - is the easiest way to understand and communicate them. Most statistics are presented at electoral ward level because this is how the census does it and this can make it easier for you. You may feel that all this information collection and its presentation are a big chore if you have already decided the service you want to provide, but it is very useful information for making the case to potential funders or supporters. Your case could be demolished if you did not know that there was a similar day centre down the road or that population figures do not support your case for a new service.

All this preliminary work is best done by the group who are going to do the planning for the service, but sometimes you have to assemble a new group after the initial phase. It is worth considering the membership carefully. Busy people are always the best, they know how to get things done and they have the contacts. Obviously an interdisciplinary group is needed, but you might like to think about co-opting potential opposition in order to avoid later sabotage. Carers are always needed not only for their undoubted expertise but because they will be the people to give your service credibility in the eyes of other carers.

When you are thinking about the kind of service you consider would meet the needs you have identified, it is always worth going to have a look at other similar services and trying to talk to some of the committee to see how they managed to get things going. There is a dire shortage of service evaluation studies but it is worth checking this out. You will find it useful to make a list of principles for your service: this can be a good team-building job for the planning group too. The Social Services Inspectorate has produced an excellent guide to principles in longstay care (Department of Health 1993). The Dementia Services Development Centre also has a list which is tried and tested. It is:

- small
- local
- domestic
- affordable
- accessible
- flexible
- properly designed
- can help in a crisis

- available 24 hours/seven days
- trained and supported staff
- trains, informs and empowers carers
- trains, informs and empowers people with dementia
- based on a good knowledge of the individual.

The service you are planning is unlikely to score 13 out of 13 but it is worth considering which ones are important and on which ones you would be prepared to compromise. Another useful planning exercise is the "worst possible scenario" approach. What if . . . the roof falls in; a member runs away; a volunteer gashes his hand; somebody falls in the toilet and so on.

Other essential jobs in the planning phase are deciding exactly for whom your service is intended. You would be amazed at the number of services that are set up without getting this sorted out. They end up being unable to explain to people who might make referrals who is appropriate and they also fail to gear up staff and activities tightly enough. Let us say, for example, that you are planning a day centre using a church hall. You have done your survey and your analysis and you know that the need is for day care for people who are very active, and have such troublesome behaviour that they are rejected by existing centres. To provide good care for this group of people with dementia you need a room where all members can see and be seen, a high staff ratio, lots of staff training and support and a highly interactive regime. Your members will need to be kept busy and engaged, often on a one-to-one basis and always doing things that they enjoy. This work can be hugely rewarding. By contrast, if you found the need was for day care for people with good social skills and minimal behaviour problems you could afford to be considering several smaller rooms, fewer staff and less intensive activities.

I have mentioned before the need to find a way of communicating about the needs of people with dementia and the value of using a standard dependency scale. This would be useful to sort out at this stage. If you were to use the REPDS, for example, which was described in the Assessment section in Chapter 4, you might find it useful to specify people with low dependency in terms of self-care, nursing care and psychiatric disorder and high dependency in terms of behaviour and confusion. Such a clear specification would make it very easy for people like GPs to make a referral. This can then be put in the leaflet you are going to have to produce to let people know that the service is available.

Writing up the service you intend to provide as a proposal, either for purchasers or for a grant application, is a good way to clarify exactly what it is you plan to do. You can demonstrate that you have thought it through. Costs are often the key section and need to be presented very carefully, including the items you may have at no cost. The fact that use of the church hall may be free should often be presented as the equivalent of an amount of money being given by the church. Having identified the service you want to set up and whom it is for, there is a marketing job to be done with key staff. Key staff are usually the purchasers but they may consult specialist providers for their views so you will need to have won the support of people like consultants in old age psychiatry. Even if you get a contract for certain people or for a group of people you will inevitably have to find other money, and letters of support can be invaluable. Applying for money and mobilising resources always take much longer than you expect. Sometimes small efforts like jumble sales are important just to keep the team together. There is always a point where people feel like giving up and there are always people around who will be discouraging. You may, in fact, not manage to set up the service you dream of but you will be prepared when the next opportunity comes along.

Personal survival

Perhaps this should be the first chapter of the book since the well-being of the staff will have a huge impact on the quality of the service for people with dementia and their carers. Working with these people is very stressful. In my view a lot of staff are unwilling to mention their feelings of stress because they are only too well aware that carers manage, or have managed in the past, often alone, for far more hours than any paid person. It is stressful work because people with dementia require the staff to take the initiative, to be always giving, warm and human and to be creative and imaginative. It is rarely a relationship of equal exchange although some people with dementia strive to give to a relationship, and there are great satisfactions in the work. Working with carers can be very exhausting too, since they often offload a lot of emotion and their own stress. Many situations are fraught with difficulties and worries. Dementia is a terminal illness so death and dying are inescapable.

So how do we survive? How do we keep our motivation to respond to the special-ness of each individual? How do we stay creative? In my view the first step is to ensure that we have support mechanisms. Ideally these should include col-leagues. Regular supervision or debriefing is invaluable because it makes time to reflect on practice and our own performance. Teamwork with other staff can be a source of support and ideas. In both cases we get out of them what we put in. And in both cases we have first to acknowledge that we are not superhuman. None of us cope well all the time. We all make mistakes and we all have our strengths and weaknesses. It is, in part, about trust. Nothing is more supportive than a line manager you trust and colleagues you can trust and, of course, this cannot always be the case. But it is worth testing out and putting some effort into it. If work col-leagues are not helpful, there are often support mechanisms in the community: professional lunch clubs, meetings of elderly special interest groups, even mutual support groups that meet regularly for lunch or for an hour after work.

It is important to know how to recognise stress in ourselves and to know what to do about it. Headaches, irritability, feelings of powerlessness and panic are a few of the well-known symptoms. There are numerous techniques as well as talking things through. Relaxation needs to be learnt and what works will vary from person to person. We need to learn what works for us and ensure that we take it seriously. Being able to recognise our own stress is useful in that we also need to be able to recognise when we have nothing to give to the people in our care. This may be a sudden and short-term problem, or it may be that we are just burned out. In the short term some managers are wise enough to move staff who own up to being unable to do the job for some reason. Some of us can organise our workloads to do paperwork on bad days. Sometimes colleagues will bear the weight as long as it is perceived as reciprocal.

In the longer term there may be no alternative but to stop. Some units will only take part time staff on the basis that they are fresher, have more to give and do not burn out. I have heard it asserted, and I think there is a good deal of sense in the principle, that it is not possible to give frontline care, full time, to people with dementia, for more than three years. After this, staff should go and do something else for a while or go part time. If we are constantly learning either individually or as a staff group, then we are much more likely to solve problems creatively and to remain actively involved ourselves (Senge 1990). One of the most motivating things to do is to keep learning, which is why training is the next section.

Training
It is not clear what professional background is the most appropriate for people with dementia: each trade stakes a claim. It is much more likely that we need a

mix of professions. We also need those who can respond as people to people with warmth, imagination and respect. None of these are acquired on professional courses. Some have a gift with people with dementia, and others will never have it no matter how much training you give them. Most of us are somewhere in between, and we can thrive if we are given training which inspires us to examine our practice and learn new skills. Training should consist of knowledge, skills and attitudes. The last is probably the most important and the most difficult to improve. There is a lot of ageism about training, with some managers believing that older staff will not change their attitudes. The reality is that some people are more receptive than others - always have been and always will be. The skill for managers is in identifying this potential for change and supporting it with training and back up. It is rarely worth changing the attitudes of one person in any unit and expecting them to work like yeast. There usually needs to be a group involved if there is to be any change. Much of training is about reinforcing positive attitudes and giving good strokes for good practice.

Staff often say they have no time for training. There are two answers to this. The most important is that you should not practise if you are not being constantly trained in the sense of building up skills. Dementia care is a world where new skills are emerging which can make a real difference to people with dementia and their carers. The care that we give is likely to be the only sort of "treatment" given and we have to make it as effective as possible. There are also constant new challenges. Staff in a group home for people with learning disabilities were finding it very difficult to care for Mr Young. He, like many people with Down's syndrome, got dementia in his fifties. The staff needed training about dementia care. Equally important was their need for training in sustaining their customary rehabilitation approach in the face of constant deterioration. They tended to see his need for basic physical care rather than his need for encouragement in maintaining skills. Given encouragement and having tasks broken down into small steps, Mr Young surprised the staff by what he was still able to achieve. The second answer to the "no time for training" approach is that training is in part a matter of style of management and some training can be woven into every day. We all have skills to share, or have read something we think might be useful. Case discussions, staff exchanges, demonstrating skills on the job and joint visiting are all kinds of training that can go on all the time. In a sense no manager can afford not to be constantly training if standards are to be sustained and good staff retained.

There are now very large amounts of training materials available many of which can be shared between units. Self study packs, viseos and group-based training are emerging as well as the more conventional opportunities for courses.

Chapter 6
Therapy

Therapy may seem to be an odd word to use in a book about people with dementia and their carers. Its use is quite deliberate for several reasons. First, because it speaks of a potential for growth and change in all of us, even if we have dementia. So it is used to underline the positive nature of working with people with dementia. Second, because there are all sorts of new therapies emerging. We are in the midst of an intensely exciting phase in dementia care in relation to therapy. In part, people are using the word to mean that everything we do can make people better. We can, for example, design buildings that are therapeutic: that enable people rather than disable them. We can organise regimes that stimulate people rather than simply keep them clean and alive. We are also learning that many of the therapies used with other groups of people can, with some modification, apply to people with dementia and their carers. This whole book is about therapy, if it means that we are all working to make people as well as they can be: to function at the highest possible level within the limits set by the neurological damage. It is, of course, as yet impossible to treat dementia in the sense of reversing the deterioration of the brain, but it is possible in many cases to reduce the anguish and pain. It may be possible before too long to prescribe a drug which slows or perhaps even stops further progression of brain disease in some forms of Alzheimer's disease. There is nothing yet on the horizon for other kinds of dementia and it will be several years before any drug is widely available.

In my job I visit a great many facilities providing care for people with dementia. Many staff tell me that the people in their centre or unit are "too seriously demented" or "too far gone" to benefit from any kind of therapy. This seems to me to say much more about the staff than about the residents. The staff have clearly run out of ideas. They are probably feeling a lack of support, recognition and training. They may be burnt out or demoralised. There is always something that can be done to engage the feelings of someone with dementia even if it is only through touch or music: responding to both of which seems to occur despite considerable neurological damage. It is too easy to "blame" people with dementia for not responding. In this chapter I want to concentrate on work which is traditionally put under the heading of therapy: behaviour management, activities, counselling, group work and family therapy.

Behaviour management

Behaviour management techniques are developing very rapidly and again most of this book has been implicitly, if not explicitly, about making the behaviour of people with dementia less stressful to them as well as to everyone else. I want first to emphasise the word "stress". In my view a lot of people with dementia are highly stressed and this impairs their functioning as it does for all of us. People caring for those with dementia are often highly stressed, not least by proximity to very stressed individuals and a feeling of being powerless to help them, given this frightful disease. A first plank in any planned care must be the reduction of stress, and the plan itself should assist carers and paid staff alike. This section deals with how we might approach the planning process - first by understanding what affects behaviour. Behaviour is a result of numerous influences: internal, surrounding and in the world at large. I have tried to express this in a diagram which I know is crude and could be extended or tidied up, but which I find helpful.

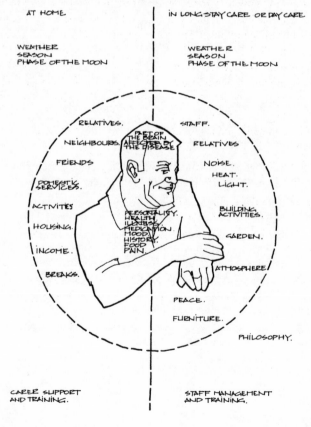

It reminds me of the multiplicity of factors we need to consider when looking at the determinants of behaviour. There is a similar diagram in Goudie and Stokes's (1990) useful book, which makes the point that behaviour is mood, thought, speech, and action.

We start in the middle of the diagram with a person who has a mind and body which are in part the ones he was born with, and in part the result of a lifetime's experience. This experience will be considerable since most people with dementia are older people. People will have had all manner of injuries, operations and stresses. They will have learnt all kinds of coping mechanisms, some more effective than others. Dementia is a stress of the first order and, in part, the way people cope with it will be a reflection of the way they have coped with other of life's events.

Current internal influences include the actual disease process: what part of the brain is being affected and to what extent. Clearly, different abilities will be affected in different people where the disease has affected different parts of the brain. There is a view that we all have a degree of cerebral reserve which enables us to cope with a degree of brain damage. The suggestion is that some people have a considerably reduced cerebral reserve so the signs of dementia are more apparent at an earlier stage. Cerebral reserve may be diminished by previous brain injury, life stress, etc. It is possible that people with learning disabilities have a diminished cerebral reserve, perhaps because it is very stressful coping with a learning disability. This might again account for as yet unproven assertions that people with low educational levels are seen to get dementia earlier. Some people claim that minority ethnic older people get dementia earlier and once again the theory of cerebral reserve may account for this, since we know that being a member of such a minority in the UK over the last fifty years has been a stressful business.

It is clear that the sort of person you were will to an extent affect the way your dementia shows itself, but some people dispute this. It is, of course, impossible to accurately determine the cause of anyone's behaviour, and I am only suggesting a range of reasons that might be useful to consider in working out ways of understanding behaviour. The effect of previous personality then needs to be on the list.

Defences can diminish in old age. It is possible that some of the behaviour we now see is the result of traumas in the past. The memories have been well suppressed throughout life but, without the defences, the memory comes to the fore. This seems to be true of the people who survived horrors of war, who are unable to block out the memories in old age and are sometimes profoundly mentally ill.

Staff have reported occasions where it was clear that a resident had been sexually abused in the past, a fact unknown to relatives. The dementia led to the resident being unable to suppress the memory, and her behaviour indicated that this memory was still very vivid.

Current health and medication are crucial determinants of behaviour. Constipation affects everyone's behaviour whether or not they have dementia, but it is often overlooked as an explanation. Earlier in this book I mentioned the importance of distinguishing an acute confusional state from a dementia, since it is often caused by illness and stress. This can of course occur on top of a dementia. The behaviour of a person with dementia will deteriorate very sharply if they have, for example, a urinary tract infection. They may be unable to tell you about it. Pain affects everyone's behaviour and we need to be alert to the possibility that someone's behaviour is telling us about their pain: psychological or physical.

Medication is a major factor and anyone who has worked in a psychogeriatric or geriatric assessment unit will have stories of the dramatic improvement in people who are taken off their drug cocktails.

Mood and food are important internal factors. People with dementia seem acutely sensitive to the mood of others and will often pick up that of relatives or staff instinctively. Sour and unhappy staff will often have sour and unhappy residents and vice versa. At the start of this section I mentioned stress. Stressed staff equals stressed people with dementia. Staff who are confident and working to a plan of care alongside colleagues and carers implementing the same plan will be less stressed.

Food is a major issue, though little is known about the immediate effect of different kinds of food on behaviour. I have already mentioned the view that, for some people, behaviour is affected by blood sugar levels and that if you want a steady level of behaviour you need to provide very regular amounts of high calorie food, perhaps every two hours, rather than big meals three times a day. Certainly the mealtimes can affect behaviour profoundly for the better or the worse depending on whether they are a source of enjoyment or stress. Dehydration is a factor which needs to be on the agenda for consideration.

Stress itself is another factor for people with dementia. A failing memory and a diminishing ability to work things out must be stressful whether or not the environment is stressful. We are learning to diminish stress by reducing stimulation overload, such as noise, keeping the atmosphere calm, using techniques such as massage and so on. I was visiting a thirty-bedded dementia unit recently. Staff had made considerable efforts to divide the residents into small groups. Some were actively playing bingo, others were sitting in the conservatory, others were sleeping. The staff seemed quite unaware of the potentially stressful impact of old-time dance music which played for the whole hour I was in the unit. Nobody seemed to be listening. I did not get the impression that the staff had checked that everyone in the unit really liked old-time dance music, let alone having it on all the time. It is ironic that some of the most disturbed people with dementia are cared for in the most stressful environments: big, noisy, confusing places with little personalised care. Many units have hard floors and wall surfaces that amplify noise in addition to the usual racket of trolleys, voices, doors, etc. If a person in these units shouts all the time, the other residents and staff really suffer.

In the immediate environment we have another set of factors which may influence behaviour: noise, heat, cold, light, dark, space. The design of the building has been mentioned in a previous chapter. Other people who live in and, in longstay and day care settings, who work in the building are bound to have an impact. The total lack of people where the person with dementia lives alone may affect behaviour. Inside, outside, peace and activity: all can affect behaviour. This is no different from the rest of us, it is just that the person with dementia may not be able to work out what is causing them to behave in a certain way and may not be able to control their behaviour.

In the outer environment we have weather and the seasons. The season may be particularly important. We are now all well aware of the way that the lack of sunlight can affect some people and it may well be that certain sufferers of dementia who spend a lot of winter time inside are also adversely affected. Referrals to psychiatric services seem to increase during autumn and winter, in part because carers cannot take their relatives out because of poor weather.

If all these are candidates for the key factor affecting behaviour, how on earth do we decide which to opt for? The answer is careful monitoring of the difficult behaviour. What seems to happen just before it and just after it. Asking the question WHY? is the first step to behaviour management. Is Mr Jones very aggressive at a particular time of day? when with a particular member of staff? before or after food? when confronted with a particular activity? and so on. Then the next step is to try changing possible causative factors. Some people are very imaginative about this.

Mrs Beale was the widow of a naturalist and she would not settle in her nursing home. She headed out through the door at every possible moment. One of the staff made the suggestion that she was used to watching animals and birds so they bought a bird table and she was given food to stock it. She has not wandered since. Mr McDonald was urinating all over the residential home even though he had an en suite WC. A bucket solved the problem for him. It turned out that he had been a shepherd who was quite unaccustomed to internal sanitary facilities. These two examples emphasise the importance of the past because this is so often neglected but it would be possible to provide numerous examples where daily routine was the key. Mrs Aubrey, for example, would not eat meals at a table with the other patients in her longstay ward. She was thoroughly objectionable at mealtimes. A constant supply of finger food was the answer for her.

If the behaviour is the result of brain damage alone then there may be less to be done except medication but in most cases there is something which can be done which will reduce, though not always eliminate, behaviour, unless of course it is the person's usual personality. Planned intervention and a consistent approach by all the key people are essential. If Mr Brown gets upset and abusive if he is rushed with his food, then it is important that his daughter and her husband know this so that they can organise the days they look after him to give Mrs Brown a rest. The day centre also needs to know this as does the residential home which provides the respite. Similarly if Mrs Miller is very agitated whenever she is asked a direct question which she cannot answer, then it is important that everyone who relates to her knows this.

Activities
Activities are a central part of any therapeutic regime, even one happening in the person's home. There are a lot of uses of activities:

- assessment
- behaviour management
- maintaining cognitive function and skills
- enhancing self-esteem
- sociability
- recreation and relaxation.

Most people think of activities as recreation in the sense of passing the time enjoyably, but this is a very limited view. Some people go further and think that activities are the responsibility of only one profession: occupational therapy. In my view, almost anything you do with people with dementia is an activity which can be purposeful, planned and therapeutic.

For many people with dementia, especially in group settings, the day is profoundly boring. There is a lot of sitting and sleeping, interrupted by brief spurts of organised activity, and meals. People with dementia are often described as apathetic, which is a rather negative way of describing the hesitant uncertainty and lack of confidence so often exhibited. Others are more active but often in a chaotic and sometimes disruptive fashion. It is almost always necessary for staff to take the lead, which is why this work is so exhausting. You have to give so much of yourself, all the time. It is because what happens has to be planned and initiated by staff that it is referred to as "activities". What happens does not happen naturally; we are responsible for each individual and for the group as a whole.

So with a number of waking hours to fill as therapeutically as possible, where do we start? We start by knowing a great deal about the people with dementia: their backgrounds and preferences. We know how they would like to pass the day ideally even if we cannot tailor the whole day for them. I use the term "day" here whilst being very aware that in some longstay settings for some people the night is more important. Miss Burton was an ex-night sister from the local hospital. When in the nursing home, she maintained her familiar routine: she slept all day and got up at night to eat and spent the time with the night staff.

Knowing people's preferences can be daunting. Mr Grant liked to be on his own listening to classical music. Mrs Beattie preferred big band music on all the time and she liked good, boisterous conversation. Mrs MacLeod liked Gaelic psalm singing. Mrs Corriere spoke only Italian and liked to sing along with opera. It is a very great deal easier if people with dementia are in small, relatively homogeneous groups. Mrs MacLeod was actually in a Gaelic-speaking day centre where they sing psalms all day. Mrs Corriere's day centre alternated English-speaking days with Italian-speaking days, since it was in the midst of an Italian community in Victoria. It is also a great deal easier if there are enough staff or volunteers to allow for individual attention and one-to-one activities for some people some of the time. Relatives' involvement in longstay care can provide this highly individual attention. Mr Peters relatives came and sang Bach chorale music with him and even in his advanced dementia he could manage to join in.

Some preferences are gender based and since most settings have a predominance of women, there is little offered to men. Some men are uncomfortable being with women at all or to any extent, most of their lives having been conducted in the company of other men. In these communities, such as a fishing village in the west of Scotland, a room where the men can be together is really essential if they are to enjoy the time. A day centre for younger people with dementia found that their men came much more regularly and willingly than the women. The activities were therefore geared to their interests. The staff thought this happened because these were all men who were accustomed to being out of the house all day at work.

Another set of considerations is related to the stage of dementia. There have been some very useful advances recently in providing experiences for people in the last stages of dementia using every possible sense: light, warmth, touch, music, smell; altogether in as relaxing and enjoyable a way as possible. An example of this is the Snoezelen rooms (Benson 1994), originally developed for people with very severe learning disabilities. Carers and staff who accompany the person with dementia have been seen to benefit too, perhaps because of the relaxing experience itself and perhaps because they feel they are doing something for the dementia sufferer. The sense of helplessness felt by many staff caring for people in the last stages of dementia can be very demoralising.

Another characteristic of a therapeutic approach is that activities should be failure free. This is a real challenge. As well as maintaining cognitive and other skills they have to be achievable. Mr Hamson had always been a workaholic and needed to feel he was doing something useful. He would sort postcards into countries. It did not matter how long it took him or indeed if he did it wrong. Mr Burns "helped" his wife by sorting the grit and brown bits of lentils. We have all seen people with dementia playing games in centres where, for example, they have to throw a bean bag onto a dart-board-type mat. In the group there are often people who have no idea what to do and no understanding. For them the game exacerbates their sense of failure especially when the other participants get irritated. Much more appropriate for many people are familiar games such as bingo with staff alongside the less able. Playing for money will add to the familiarity! For others it will be dominoes.

It is our responsibility to make the day (or night) enjoyable as far as possible. Some people ask why this is important if the person with dementia forgets almost immediately. This is to deny that the person with dementia has feelings. They may not remember why they are relaxed and cheerful but they certainly have the feelings.

Let us look at one activity to see how it can meet the objectives outlined above. Preparation of food in a day centre can be the main morning activity in which everyone participates. First there is the discussion over coffee about the meal, linking it to other meals. "Today we are having broth followed by mince and potatoes" leads to all kinds of memories for some people. Then there are a whole set of chores which can be tailored to meet the skills of the members, after the hand washing, which is an activity in itself. Some people can wash the vegetables standing up at the sink. Some can peel them. Peeling onions is more difficult than potatoes and some do not enjoy the tears. Some can check the barley for bits. Others can chop on a board at the table. Staff will know who can handle a sharp knife. Perhaps, like Mr di Rollo in Chapter 2, one of the men was a chef. Some people like to stir. Time is not an issue. This can take a good hour or two with lots of talk, lots of reassurance and lots of voiced appreciation for a job well done. Some appropriate music from time to time might add to the enjoyment, perhaps during stops for tea and coffee.

What else can be achieved through an activity like this? First assessment: people are being assessed for improvements and deterioration in tasks with which they are familiar. They will have no sense that they are being tested and found wanting. There will be potential for assessing memory, co-ordination, concentration and sociability. Second, behaviour management: some people will have been given chores in such a way that they are distracted from their difficult behaviour, others to enhance their strengths. A very agitated person might be best alongside a member of staff handing things out or stirring. A person who is very withdrawn can be given a job to do alongside others but not as part of a group. Remembering to give appreciation for the efforts of withdrawn people, however small, is especially important. Third, maintaining cognitive function and skills: reading the recipe book, weighing the ingredients and so on. There are a range of mental skills for all levels within the total task of meal preparation. Enhancing self-esteem is obvious because there will be something that almost everyone can do for which the staff or the others can be grateful and appreciative. There are no end of failure-free tasks. Enhanced sociability is one of the best results of this kind of work. There is no competition. All work together and there can be lots of good talking at the same time. As the smells waft from the cooker memories are stirred and appetites stimulated. Sometimes an old song will come to mind. Sometimes the meal itself may be one chosen to recall old memories: in Scotland there is much to talk about when making broth. Recreation and relaxation may be the least likely outcomes of such an activity but we all know that concentration on an enjoyable task can be one of the best ways of relaxing.

This may all sound a bit too good to be true and it may often be much more chaotic and difficult. One of the points I am trying to make is that familiar, daily chores have huge potential for purposeful, planned activity which is good for the individuals and good for the group. There are a hundred obstacles to this approach in most settings. There may be no kitchen; there may be no budget for the food that is inevitably wasted as sugar goes into the potatoes, not salt, or the cake mix falls on the floor. There may be seen to be too many risks. It may only work with small groups and so on. But it is worth fighting for. The following experience shows what is possible. Mr Channing was a big, restless, aggressive man in his longstay ward but, when transferred to a unit where he could spend the day ironing and vacuum cleaning, became a person who made a huge contribution to the unit.

This section on activities as therapy could fill a whole book and is therefore woefully inadequate. Archibald's books on activities (1990, 1993 and 1995) provide more information on this approach. I want here to conclude by mentioning the potential of life-story books, first raised in the section on written records. A life-story book can be an immensely helpful tool, first in understanding what activities are likely to be enjoyed by a particular person. Staff have a good start if they know that Mrs Bertoli sang in amateur opera or that Mrs Wang ran a take-away with her husband.

It also provides a tool for one-to-one work. Relatives are often at a loss to know what to do when they visit. Sitting side by side going through the life-story book and sharing memories can be very therapeutic. Sometimes aggressive or restless residents can be calmed by the same process with a member of staff. It provides immediate help in relating to the person with dementia as an individual. Sometimes it can be used as an activity to ease the transition from one setting to another. Mr Steele was very bewildered and upset when he arrived at the day centre and when he arrived back at home. Pictures of both places were put in his life-story book. His wife spent ten minutes or so in the morning talking about home and then about the centre, using the book. The staff of the day centre did likewise at the end of the day. Mr Steele became much calmer about the transitions.

Counselling
Counselling people with dementia and their carers is part and parcel of any work in this field, if by counselling we mean listening intently to what is being said and offering what is called unconditional positive regard. To do this we have to be able to empathise with the strong feelings of others without being too dismayed or cast down ourselves. Carers are always saying that what they need is someone to

isten to them. They know there are often no answers and that little can be done, ut they want to use the chance of talking to someone else to work out their own lans and approaches.

Ve all know the benefit of this but we sometimes forget that there are matters that annot be shared within families and that talking to a sympathetic outsider can be normously helpful. In the early stages we may have to listen to the matrimonial lifficulties, the grief as plans for the future perish, the intense ambivalence within elationships which become recognised as the difficulties mount. We may have to isten to anger, frustration and hurt as the person with dementia becomes more lependent. We may have to help people work through intense feelings of guilt vhen day care, respite care and longstay care are needed.

Jne of the advantages of good counselling is that it helps people to see situations nore clearly and face up to the implications. The Alzheimer's Society of Victoria ound they were getting a lot of carers coming in for counselling about two years ifter their relative had gone into longstay care. The carers were often worried that hey themselves had dementia. When they really talked it through it became clear hat they had never worked through their feelings of guilt at giving up caring. 'resumably, at the time all the attention was on the person with dementia and it vas nobody's job to listen to the carer working out his or her feelings. In a similar vein is the experience of chronically complaining relatives on a longstay ward vho were offered counselling. Talking through their guilt feelings, not only about elinquishing care but also about beginning to have a new life of their own, was elt to be very helpful and certainly diminished the complaints. We often see :arers as saints who are giving their all to care. What we seldom see is the imbivalence and the anger that are inevitable but often well hidden because the :arer is ashamed to mention them.

The possibility that unfinished emotional business actually corrodes our coping :apacities in time is one that underpins some of the approaches to counselling ieople with dementia. It is believed by Feil (1992), for example, that a lot of the :hallenging behaviour of people with dementia is due to pain from past unhappi-less that they cannot put into words. She suggests that if we can deal with the feelings and let people tell us about the pain, often in an allegorical way, then they vill feel better. It is well accepted that children who cannot talk about their feelings will tell us about them through play. Communicating through allegory or 1on-verbally is perhaps similar with people with dementia.

It is not easy. Making time to seize opportunities that arise for communicatio about feelings is often difficult and fluctuating lucidity means that people ofte want to talk when there is no time to listen. There are, however, times when ther are more chances of quiet communication: bath time and the middle of the nigh being two of them in longstay settings. People who have done a night shift wi know only too well that some people wake in the small hours and need to b comforted. Shared activity often provides opportunities for talking naturally an personally. Washing up together, walking together, looking at life-story book together can often make space for a good talk or a sharing of something painfu This has even been called milieu therapy when the daily routines of being togethe provide planned opportunities for personal communication and sharing.

In this section on counselling we must not forget the needs of paid staff, who ca have very strong and even more unmentionable feelings about their job, abou certain people with dementia in their care, or certain carers. They may find som intolerable. They may find that difficulties at home are making them unable t give of their best at work. They may be unable to cope with the sadness of a lot o the work. I am not proposing a full-scale psychotherapeutic counselling, bu rather opportunities for talking about their work with someone who has made tim and space for listening carefully. This is called supervision or debriefing and i can be immensely helpful. Issues raised in supervision are often resolved by dis cussing them in a problem-solving manner. Sometimes very difficult and painfu issues arise as they did for Mrs Roberts. Mrs Roberts worked in a nursing hom and seemed to be unable to cope with Mr Dryden who made suggestive remark and tried to grab her breasts when she was helping him. Mrs Roberts had bee sexually abused by her grandfather. She found talking about her feeling extremely difficult in the staff group. She was finally able to talk about her expe riences to her supervisor which she found immensely helpful.

Groupwork
Groupwork usually needs a very great deal more thought and planning than it gets Carers' groups are often seen as an obviously "good thing" without the organiser properly matching up the aims and methods. Groupwork theory has some ver useful principles which are largely ignored (Brown 1992). If, for example, yo want to run a group where carers become very close and feel able to share persona worries, then it has to be a time-limited, closed group. Sometimes the emergenc of an intimate, supportive group happens in the usual big, loose groups when clique of carers get to know each other very well. The difficulty of simply lettin it happen is that new members to such a group are not often welcome. If you wan

group where the relationships are so strong that it becomes self-sufficient, then it as again to be a closed group. The group then decides for itself what it wants to o. If you want an information-sharing group then it can be run on a meetings ormat.

he usual kind of carers' group is an odd hybrid which is meant to do everything nd does nothing well. It is meant to provide mutual support which it does at a airly superficial level unless people form friendships which go on outside the roups. It is meant to be information sharing which it does quite well except that eople seldom feel able to ask about and share their own difficulties. It is often neant to both sustain existing members and welcome new ones whereas in fact ew members of any group, where there are already strong links, will have a hard me working their way into the group. It is meant to be a group that will have the onfidence to voice opinions about the services received and their gaps, yet rarely re members given the confidence to do this. It is often meant to be a group that vill run itself, with time, and yet only in groups where people know and trust each ther well does this happen. It will rarely happen when a group is accustomed to elying on a strong professional.

n summary, groupwork skills are yet to really come into their own in this field. he book by Bender and Norris (1987) is a good place to start. As far as people vith dementia are concerned the skills are even less well developed except erhaps with people who have had an early diagnosis. There is an increasing mount of very useful literature from people who have run such groups (Yale 991). They are clearly small, intimate and very intense with what seems to be a teady membership of the same people (that is, relatively closed) who come to rust and rely on each other a great deal. Sharing both the feelings and experience bout techniques which are helpful in coping with problems like a failing memory eems to be very helpful. They are also a very good source of insight for staff into vhat are the worries of people who have been told they have dementia, at a stage vhen they are able to talk about it and make some decisions. Friel McGowin 1993), a woman with dementia, decided to help herself by helping others. She tarted a support group for other early-diagnosed people. She felt people needed elp from others "walking through the same maze".

Groups at the later stages are usually into activities such as reminiscence (Gibson 994). Most group care settings are by their very nature groupwork yet the skills nd insights from groupwork are seldom applied. I have in mind our knowledge bout the phases of a group which are, generally, a process of sounding out each other, a phase of turmoil as people feel safe enough to test the group out, and the a phase of closeness. Knowing this can be very helpful in both staff groups ar groups of residents or members. If the numbers are too big it is unlikely to fe like a group. There ought to be a great deal more work in small groups withi settings where the same people gather each day or week to do something togethe with a strong emphasis on it being special and different from the normal routin A student ran a very much enjoyed weekly group in a residential home. She calle it The Tuesday Club. Members met in one of the lounges to do some exercise and to talk together in a small group.

Family therapy
Family therapy, traditionally practised in dysfunctional families usually in relatio to distressed children, clearly has usefulness when families are under stre because one member has dementia but it is not to be undertaken without prop skills and support. However, there will be times when workers see whole familie Sometimes, the diagnosis is given to a whole family including the person wit dementia. Sometimes care planning meetings involve the whole family a agreement is worked out about who will do what, at what time. Sometimes, whe there is a crisis the whole family is assembled to try and sort it out.

Thinking of dementia as a family problem rather than a problem just for th person, or the person and the carer, can be very constructive. Sometimes yo become aware that the problem is actually elsewhere; there might, for example, b a difficult adolescent, but everyone avoids dealing with that, and is scapegoatin granny. There may be prolonged resentment that granny has had all the attentio and that husband or teenage daughter feel shortchanged. Sometimes a crisis lik dementia can bring families closer together as they struggle to provide comfo and support. Sadly this often leaves out the person with dementia who has n been told the diagnosis. Working out a care plan with a family meeting can mea that the burden is shared and less risk of one person being trapped (or choosing be trapped) in the role of main carer.

There is very little easily available literature about this potentially useful way working in the field of dementia care. Sherlock and Gardiner (1993) have writte a general introduction but there is need for a great deal more. The major therape tic advances are likely to be transfers from other fields and this is a good exampl

Chapter 7
The Future

In 1995 work with people with dementia is at a very exciting stage. There are enough enthusiasts and experts to have reached a critical mass and the momentum has started. The pace of change is thoroughly exhilarating. New kinds of services, new skills, new theories and new approaches are emerging in every country having a population with a significant proportion of very old people. The issue will be to what extent all this enthusiasm can survive the economic downturn in most countries.

Work with people with dementia and their carers is never going to be the most important public priority: that will always be children. Scotland made dementia the top priority for the Health Service for the rest of the century in 1988 (Scottish Home and Health Department) but this was very unusual indeed. In spite of population trends and service shortfalls, most countries have not given it that level of priority. A small impetus has come from the fact that younger people, especially those with AIDS or HIV, get dementia.

The less-developed world will have to face the issue of dementia before too long. Early in the next century countless people who survived the diseases of childhood are going to be in the older age groups, and a proportion will get dementia. The numbers will dwarf those in the more-developed countries and the service shortfall is of quite a different order. This, combined with the rapid urbanisation of most of these countries, makes for a lack of family networks which might just have sustained these very dependent older people. What will we want to say to them about what we have learnt in the UK?

The first principle we will want to share is that of listening to people with dementia and their carers. In this country we have, on the whole, let professionals do the planning. A lot of dedicated professionals, with all the best intentions, have developed very interesting and valuable services but they have frequently not incorporated the qualities that are valued by carers, such as flexibility, and ability to offer a twenty-four-hour/seven day service. It is quite clear, when you look at a lot of our services, that they are, on the whole, run for the convenience of staff. Day care, for example, is invariably during the working day and yet a lot of carers really struggle to get the person with dementia ready for picking up at 9.30. They would find it a lot easier to take the morning slowly and then have the afternoon and evening to themselves. We offer respite care in set blocks, which is much easier to plan for and often far more than the person really needs. Alternate weekends off, or overnight once a week to allow carers to maintain a hobby, might be much more valuable.

In Britain we seem to struggle all the time to make services client-centred. We seem to find it very difficult to really listen to, and respect, the judgement of carers, and to make our services adaptable to individual needs. There seems to be a tendency to slip backwards all the time to an easier option. Perhaps this is a fact of life. I am inclined to think it is also about professional arrogance - that we have to believe we know best to justify the fact that we earn a salary for what we do.

Yet really listening and providing precisely what people need is a very complicated and difficult job. It requires enormous skill. Another explanation may be the low esteem enjoyed by this field of work. This results in people feeling they are doing a mundane job because everyone around them, including, sadly, their managers in a lot of cases, think that caring for people with dementia is a mundane job. Society's ageism and sexism are behind this. Most younger people prefer not to think about ageing and dementia, which they achieve by seeing older people as a different and less worthy species. How else can we explain the toleration of the profoundly boring and unstimulating regimes in many large nursing homes and longstay wards, for example?

So, as a first principle, we should want to be saying to people who are just starting on the road of caring for a significant number of people with dementia in their society: carers and people with dementia are the experts first and foremost. They know what they need and, to a degree, it will be different in each case, so services must be adaptable to individual needs.

The principle of putting the wishes of the customer first is related to the somewhat off-putting concepts of customer care which are so omnipresent in all the successful service industries, such as hotels and car exhaust replacers. It seems that, in service industries, if you are not constantly training staff and giving them incentives for customer care, they quickly revert to a lower level. In a sense I am saying that staff are the equivalent of the machine in manufacturing and they all need the same degree of maintenance!

We might also want to say something about the status of dementia care. Given how much we have learnt in the last few years about the potential of skilled services we need to be saying loud and clear that this is a field of care requiring the highest levels of skill. This is not just because we are working with older people and they deserve the best, but that we know that our skills and expertise are the treatment required. What I mean is that we know people with dementia are acutely sensitive to the social and the built environments. Their behaviour and well-being depend just as much on where and the way they are treated as they do on medication. Therefore to ensure that people function at the highest possible level within the parameters of neurological damage, all the skills and expertise we have acquired are essential. What look like normal housekeeping tasks, for example, are instead an individual plan of activities to achieve maximum competence and confidence of the person. What looks like an informal gathering of carers is in fact a skilful use of groupwork principles. What looks like a nice homely environment is in fact a very carefully designed building which helps people to find their way whenever possible.

So the second thing we should want to say is that this is not dead-end work for staff unable to function in other settings. It is a highly skilled and challenging task where staff need constant training, high quality management support and recognition of their skills.

Related to this is the third thing we should want to say, which is the need to embrace the new culture of dementia care: one that is positive and rehabilitative. It is no longer possible to consider that people with dementia are so unaware of their environment that it does not matter what it is like. We need to actively discourage the building of large longstay units away from the communities from which people originate and away from the people with whom they feel most comfortable. We also need to seize the initiative, to a sensible degree, from the medics. The new culture of dementia care has to be based on a team approach, as does all rehabilitative care. Conversely, we have to ensure that an appropriate degree of medical expertise is available, both for the diagnosis and input on the brain disease and also on treatment of concomitant physical conditions, the symptoms of which we know can be wrongly attributed to the neurological damage.

This relates to the fourth piece of advice we would want to give, which is about the way services are organised. The split between health care and social care is very damaging to people with dementia. They have needs which are complex, rapidly changing and an inseparable combination of health and social needs. Our system of care makes difficulties where none need to exist. It is in part about a power struggle between health and welfare organisations where each is trying to ensure maximum control over resources whilst at the same time playing "pass the parcel" with people whose needs do not fit tidily into their remit.

I think we should also want to say that the first focus of attention, as far as caring organisations are concerned, should be on the frontline. This means, as I said above, that you start with carers. Are they as trained, informed and supported as they can be? It means that the most important staff to be trained and supported are those in primary care such as GPs and community nurses, and staff such as home helps, social workers and day care staff. If they are giving a skilled and well-supported service, which allows them to offer flexible and responsive care, then the vast bulk of people with dementia, those who are living at home, will be well served. I say this with mixed feelings because it is my experience that managers of services are often less up to date than their staff. They trained a relatively long time ago and are often unaware of the new culture and approach, so fail to support their staff who take this approach. In some ways, targeting them for training makes sense but the impact on the individual and their family will be less.

This concentration on the frontline is often on staff providing services in the community generally, for whom dementia is far from their main responsibility. GPs, for example, probably only have eight patients with moderate to severe dementia living at home, in an average-sized caseload in a community with a normal age spread in the population (Philp 1989). Yet if they are not trained there will not be early diagnosis, which can be so helpful to families who want to be able to sort themselves out whilst they are able and to make plans for the future. There will also not be a sufficient early referral to services, nor the sustained support which carers need so badly over the months and years.

Similarly, the home help service is rarely specialist, yet if home helps are trained in dementia care they can help people seek a diagnosis and can provide the necessary advice on where to go for help. Their skills in communication may well be essential in helping people with dementia and their carers down the rocky path ahead. Non-specialist services are inevitably the way most people will be cared for. There are far too many people with dementia needing help for specialist services to be a reality for more than a tiny minority. We need to ensure that all staff who come in contact with people with dementia and their carers are well trained and briefed, not just those in specialist services.

This raises the issue about who gets specialist services and when. This is a dilemma for which there is no easy answer. It will be less of a dilemma if the normal run of service providers are trained and able to offer appropriate help up to a certain level. But some people will need specialist care because their needs are so complex. Often this relates to challenging behaviour. Yet this is not straightforward. The dilemma hinges on the question of whether people move to get help or services move to them. Obviously the latter is preferable, but often the behaviour is such that more help does not solve the problem. The next issue is what happens when the specialist unit has sorted out the behaviour. Should the person return to where they were before? Perhaps their behaviour will simply deteriorate again. There are also people who passionately believe that you need to provide the specialist service when the person still has some real learning potential so they can adapt to it. It is very hard to give any firm advice on these issues. It will be different for different people but this is a hard, and often expensive, way to plan services. Ideally a range of options is needed. Some people will benefit from a move. Indeed, moving to somewhere better usually has a good outcome so, within reason, moving in itself is not necessarily to be avoided.

There are also issues about maintaining the quality of specialist services. They can become a dumping ground and full of demoralised staff who feel neglected and taken for granted. Conversely, they can be wonderful resources of expertise where training and placements are offered and much appreciated. Much of what we know today was learnt in specialist settings which set out to show that a positive approach can really affect the experience of this disease for all concerned. In a sense, like everything else, it is the reasons for the specialism that are the key. If they exist to take problems off the street to hide them away, then they will be awful. If they exist to offer a rehabilitative service to certain individuals, who go there for good reasons, they are more likely to be therapeutic in style. Perhaps at least one specialist service is required in every locality to show what can be done and to be a local resource. If this is to be a policy, then this specialist service needs to be multipurpose, offering a flexible range of services for people with dementia and their carers. So the advice here needs to be something like: concentrate first on raising the levels of expertise in all frontline staff, and set up specialist services for very clear reasons.

We might want to say something about the law. Ours is so very clumsy with its all-or-nothing approach of competent or incompetent. A mechanism for making judgements about degrees and areas of competence which would also make judgements when there were very complex conflicts of interest would be very useful. It would need to be one which was not so expensive or elaborate that nobody used it.

Finally, I think we should want to say something about public awareness. A well-informed public is a huge asset. It also should understand that this is a devastating illness for both people with dementia and their families. It is an illness and not part of normal ageing; it also should understand that it needs to be talked about, that we have really suffered in the UK because people are ashamed of this disease and tend to hide it. If dementia was easier to talk about then people would come forward for an earlier diagnosis and for help. There might be more public understanding, so that it was understood as a disease and not something of which to be ashamed. There might even be more attention to the needs of those with dementia and their carers.

It would be ideal to educate the public to see it as a form of disability and to understand that the attitudes which people with dementia and their carers encounter are as disabling as the disease itself, which is the case with most other disabilities.

The public have to appreciate that there is plenty that can be done for people with dementia and their carers. We do not know how to stop the disease but we increasingly know how to make it less frightful for all the parties involved. Hospices have managed to change attitudes in this respect very successfully. Nobody thinks that hospices are a waste of money, yet people die in hospices. This is because the public respect the personhood of the dying; they see real people and they see themselves. We need to make sure this is also true of people with dementia because it is just as true. One in ten of us will get dementia if we live into our sixties and over.

This hypothetical exercise of talking to someone from a less developed country is, in part, only making a point about the distance we in the UK have to travel before our services are as good as we know how to make them at the moment. Less developed countries are unlikely to have the resources to set up many services. What they can learn from us is what not to do and what sort of direction they might best go.

I think that we must first and foremost have to admit what we do not know. The world of dementia care has changed radically over the last five years but in some ways it has only shown us what we do not yet know. We are only just beginning to learn, for example, about ways of meeting the spiritual and sexual needs of people with dementia and we know almost nothing about minority ethnic groups and dementia and the impact of dementia if you live in an alien culture. Many blinkers have fallen away from our eyes but mainly only to reveal what an enormous journey of learning we still have to make. At least we can now travel with a degree of optimism. It will be a long but surely rewarding journey for all of us.

Bibliography

Age Concern (1995) *Your Rights* London: Age Concern England

Allan K (1994) *Wandering* Stirling: Dementia Services Development Centre

Alzeheimer's Disease Society (1995) *Dementia in the Community. Management Strategies for General Practice.*

Andrews K (1991) *Rehabilitation of the Older Adult* Kent: Edward Arnold

Archibald C (1990) *Activities* Stirling: Dementia Services and Development Centre

Archibald C (1993) *Activities II* Stirling: Dementia Services and Development Centre

Archibald C (1994) *Sexuality and Dementia: A Guide* Stirling: Dementia Services and Development Centre

Archibald C (1994) *Sexuality and Dementia: Video and Training Handbook* Stirling: Dementia Services and Development Centre

Archibald C and Murphy C (1995) *Not "Them and Us" - Simply Us!* Stirling: Dementia Services and Development Centre

BASW (1990) Guidelines for Action on Abuse of Elderly People *Social Work Today* 27 September 1990

Bell N (1992) Pink Doors and Door Knockers Stirling: Dementia Services Development Centre

Bender M and Norris A (1987) *Groupwork with the Elderly - Principles and Practices* Bicester: Winslow Press

Benson S (1994) Sniff and doze therapy *Journal of Dementia Care* 2(1), 12-14

Brown A (1992) *Groupwork* 3rd Edition Hants: Ashgate

Cohen U and Day K (1993) *Contemporary Environments for People with Dementia* Baltimore: The Johns Hopkins University Press

Corser A, Toner H and Turvey T (1991) *Behaviour Ratings For Psychogeriatric In-Patients Part 1 - An Interim Report on Crichton (ECBRS) Survey Data* Fife: Stratheden Hospital

Dant T, Cawley M, Gearing B and Johnson M (1989) *Coordinating Care: the final report of the Care for Elderly People at Home Project, Gloucester* Milton Keynes: Open University

Davis R (1993) *My Journey into Alzheimer's Disease* Amersham-on-the-Hill: Scripture Press

Department of Health, Social Services Inspectorate (1993) *Inspecting for quality: standards for the residential care of elderly people with mental disorders* HMSO: London

Feil N (1992) *Validation: The Feil Method* Ohio: Edward Feil Productions

Forster M (1989) *Have the Men Had Enough?* London: Chatto

Friel McGowin D (1993) *Living in the Labyrinth: A personal journey through the maze of Alzheimer's* USA: Elder Books

Gibson F (1991) *People with Dementia - The Ferrard Approach To Care* Edinburgh: HMSO

Gibson F (1994) *Reminiscence and Recall* London: Age Concern

Gibson F (1991) *The Lost Ones* Stirling: Dementia Services Development Centre

Goudie F and Stokes G (1990) *Working With Dementia* Bicester: Winslow Press

Hughes C P *et al* (1982) A New Clinical Scale for the Staging of Dementia *British Journal of Psychiatry* 140, 556

Ignatieff M (1993) *Scar Tissue* London: Chatton and Windus

Jacques A (1992) *Understanding Dementia* (2nd Ed) Edinburgh: Churchill Livingstone

Jorm A F and Korten A E (1988) A method for calculating projected increases in the number of dementia sufferers *Australian and New Zealand Journal of Psychiatry* 22(2), 183-189

Kitwood T and Benson S (1995) T*he New Culture of Dementia Care* London: Hawker Publications

Kitwood T and Bredin K (1992) *Person to Person* Essex: Gale Centre Publications

Langan J and Means R (1995) *Personal Finances, Elderly People with Dementia and the 'New' Community Care* Oxford: Anchor Housing Association

Levin E, Moriarty J and Gorbach P (1994) *Better for the Break* London: HMSO

Levin J and Meredith M (1988) *Daughters who care: daughters caring for mothers at home* London: Routledge

Lindesay J *et al* (1991) The Domus Philosophy: A Comparative Evaluation of a New Approach to Residential Care for the Demented Elderly *International Journal of Geriatric Psychiatry* 6(10), 727-736

Mair A (1972) *Report of Subcommittee of the Standing Medical Advisory Committee, Scottish Health Service Council on Medical Rehabilitation* Edinburgh: HMSO

Marshall M and Dixon M (1995) *Social Work with Older People* Basingstoke: Macmillan

Martin F (1992) *Every House You'll Ever Need: A Design Guide for Barrier Free Housing* Edinburgh: Edinvar Housing Association

Mattingly S (1981) *Rehabilitation Today in Great Britain* London: Update Books

McCulloch A E (1995) *Monklands Home and the REPDS* Stirling: Dementia Services Development Centre

McWalter G T *et al* (1994) Needs and needs assessment: their components and definitions with reference to dementia *Health and Social Care in the Community* 2(4), 213-219

Murphy C J (1994) *"It Started with A Sea Shell": Life story work and people with dementia* Stirling: Dementia Services Development Centre

Murphy E (1986) *Dementia and Mental Illness in the Old* London: Papermac

Nolan M R, Grant G and Ellis N C (1990) Stress is in the eye of the beholder: reconceptionalising the measurement of care burden *Journal of Advanced Nursing* 15, 544-555

Oliver M (1990) *The Politics of Disablement* Basingstoke: Macmillan

Peppard N R (1991) *Special Needs Dementia Units* New York: Springer Publishing

Phair L and Good V (1995) *Dementia: A Positive Approach* London: Scutari Press

Philp I (1989) Challenges of Dementia to the GP: five areas to attack *Geriatric Medicine* Nov, 19-29

Pritchard J (1992) *The Abuse of Elderly People: A hand book for professionals* London: Jessica Kingsley

Scottish Home and Health Department: Scottish Health Service Planning Council (1988) *Scottish Health Authorities Review of Priorities for the Eighties and Nineties (SHARPEN)* Edinburgh: HMSO

Secretaries of State for Health, Social Security, Wales and Scotland (1989) *Caring for People* London: HMSO

Senge P (1990) *The Fifth Discipline: The Art and Practice of the Learning Organisation* London: Century Business

Sherlock J and Gardiner I (1993) Systemic Family Intervention in Chapman Marshall A and M (Eds) *Dementia: New Skills for Social Workers* London: Jessica Kingsley

Yale R (1991) *A Guide to Facilitating Support Groups for Newly Diagnosed Alzheimer's Patients* San Francisco: Yale R

USEFUL ADDRESSES

Age Concern England
Astral House
1268 London Road
London SW16 4ER
Tel: 0181 679 8000

Age Concern Northern Ireland
3 Lower Crescent
Belfast BT7 1NR
Tel: 01232 245 729

Age Concern Scotland
113 Rose Street
Edinburgh EH2 3DT
Tel: 0131 220 3345

Age Concern Wales
4th Floor, 1 Cathedral Road
Cardiff CF1 9SD
Tel: 01222 371 566

Alzheimer's Disease Society
(England, Wales and N Ireland)
2nd Floor, Gordon House
10 Greencoat Place
London SW1P 1PH
Tel: 0171 306 0606

Alzheimer's Scotland - Action on Dementia
8 Hill Street, Edinburgh EH2 3JZ
Tel: 0131 225 1453

Carers National Association
11 Queens Crescent
Glasgow G4 9AS
Tel: 0141 333 9495

Carers National Association
3rd Floor
113 University Street
Belfast BT7 1HP
Tel: 01232 439843

Carers National Association
20-25 Glasshouse Yard
London EC1A 4JS
Tel: 0171 490 8818

Carers National Association
Puntglas Industrial Estate
Bedwas
Newport
Gwent NP1 8DR
Tel: 01222 880176

Dementia Services Development Centre
University of Stirling
Stirling FK9 4LA
Tel: 01786 467740

Freedom to Care
Whistle-blowers Campaigning Group
PO Box 125
West Molesey KT8 1YE

Hospice Information Service
St Christopher's Hospice
51-59 Lawrie Park Road
Sydenham, London SE26 6DZ
Tel: 0181 778 9252

MIND (National Association for Mental Health)
Granta House
15-19 Broadway
Stratford, London E15 4BQ
Tel: 0181 519 2122

Northern Ireland Association for Mental Health
80 University Street
Belfast BT7 1HE
Tel: 01232 328 474

Scottish Association for Mental Health
38 Gardiners Crescent
Edinburgh EH3 8DG
Tel: 0131 229 9687

Welsh Association for Mental Health
23 St Mary's Street
Cardiff CF1 2AA
Tel: 01222 395 123

Index